Ollie
& Ada

W0006694

Ollie & Ada

JOSEPH BURCH

The Book Guild Ltd

First published in Great Britain in 2021 by
The Book Guild Ltd
9 Priory Business Park
Wistow Road, Kibworth
Leicestershire, LE8 0RX
Freephone: 0800 999 2982
www.bookguild.co.uk
Email: info@bookguild.co.uk
Twitter: @bookguild

Copyright © 2021 Joseph Burch

The right of Joseph Burch to be identified as the author of this
work has been asserted by him in accordance with the
Copyright, Design and Patents Act 1988.

All rights reserved. No part of this publication may be
reproduced, transmitted, or stored in a retrieval system, in any form or by any means,
without permission in writing from the publisher, nor be otherwise circulated in
any form of binding or cover other than that in which it is published and without
a similar condition being imposed on the subsequent purchaser.

This work is entirely fictitious and bears no resemblance to any persons living or dead.

Typeset in 11pt Minion Pro

Printed on FSC accredited paper
Printed and bound in Great Britain by 4edge Limited

ISBN 978 1913913 519

British Library Cataloguing in Publication Data.
A catalogue record for this book is available from the British Library.

To Charlie, Jasper, Raffy and Federica.
In memory of Mum.

Contents

January

Ada

The morning light reflects the canal surface, causing my tired eyes to squint. The time is just before 6am. Quiet and stillness consumes the air. That peace will soon be shattered by morning commuters, but for now, sheer silence. I sit with my head between my knees against a cold, hard, graffiti-covered wall and pull out my favourite photo of Daisy and I. We are at Glastonbury Festival in front of the Pyramid Stage with excitement etched upon our glittered faces as we eagerly await the evening's main act. I look at her neat black bob and sparkly eyes. Tears dampen my leopard-print tights. I take a large bite of my soggy croissant and help it down with a swig of tea, the tea so weak, I taste only the milk.

I had never seen human ashes prior to Daisy's, the remains of her body dark in colour but light in density and coarse like sand. I slowly run my fingers round the insides of the tub and touch her a final time. She had sat safely sealed in an unglamorous burgundy tub, housed within a Reebok Classic shoebox beneath my bed for weeks, but I knew now was time to set her free.

Daisy loved the canal. We would come here most mornings and put the world to rights. We would talk work, relationships, music, family, our hopes and dreams, with no stone left unturned. I think back to these conversations and panic knowing we will never again share our thoughts, words and woes. She was my playmate and role model, my relationship advisor and fashion guru. She was the sister I never had. Daisy had a laugh so wicked; you would hear it before seeing her. I smile at the memory of my best friend and think back to the time we were asked to leave a Soho restaurant owing to Daisy's thunderous laugh. She was twenty-nine years young when cancer stole her. When Daisy died, part of me died too.

I scatter her ashes and watch as her tiny fragments leave me. I spread my fingers and run them through the water, weeping uncontrollably as my best friend departs. I so desperately wish I could dive into the water and scoop up Daisy's dismantled remains and piece my best friend back up together, taking her to the safety of the home we once shared. There is so much left to say, so many words unsaid. There is so much wine to drink and so many places to see. As I walk back to my flat, the rain begins to fall. I increase my pace as if my speed will make my loss smaller. Each step I take I feel her absence. I look back to the canal and in that moment, I know exactly where to find Daisy and where she will always be.

Every day we make decisions: How we wish to spend our lives, our time, whom we wish to share it with. Different opportunities stare us in the face. It's what we do with them that counts. We are immersed in routine and our lives are structured by deadlines and timescales. We rarely get to do as we choose. We seldom get to do what we enjoy, what make us truly happy, what makes us truly content. I wish I had spent more time with Daisy.

To avoid disappointment, I keep expectations low. My aspirations are average and my failures frequent. I am overdrawn, overworked and underpaid. Nobody expects much from me. I ask for little in return. My sorrow and resentment are more significant than my happiness and joy. I lack passion. I have never thrived; I am yet to flourish. I am selfish and more often than not, sad. I long for love.

I am yet to achieve anything remarkable. I am neither brave nor beautiful. My life is an orchestra of anguish. My heart needs help, my temper a tweak and my loneliness a sabbatical. I have scruffy black-tyre hair and guitar-string thin limbs. I am unlucky in life and unlucky in love. My longest time in a relationship is a paltry nine weeks.

I live alone and can count my friends on just one hand. I crave for someone to make my heart beat like a busker's banjo, to end my aimless, endless angst. I rent a small studio flat in a decaying sprawling estate. I have a degree in English literature. I sell life insurance. I remember unimportant things but forget important things. I have never done anything to be proud of. I stray very rarely from the line. I have no confessions. I have little obsessions. I drink too much. My dreams are black, my days are plagued by loneliness.

I dream of love. I dream of someone. I long for someone to patch the hole in my heart to make my insecurities cease. A soul with whom I could share a cigarette. Someone to make my world make sense, a person capable of blowing a kiss to blur my vision. I long for intimacy, trust, something, anything to mend my misery and broken soul. Somebody to leave a soppy love note by my lonely pillow even if the content were only half true.

I don't sleep well. I haven't since she left. Grief wears many faces and keeps unsociable hours. Daisy died a hard death from an aggressive cancer. The agreement at my workplace permits a week's leave for bereavement. I'm unsure how five days' leave fits for the bereaved. I still feel numb four months on. I was not ready to get out of bed after five days yet am expected to contribute to the next strategic planning meeting. My grief is not able to be neatly packed and packaged into five days' leave. Modern life has no time for grief. I still have bills to pay. I wake and walk to the bathroom, staring at the mirror and urging myself to carry on, get dressed and go to work. My only benefit of being at work is that I am not here at home alone, wallowing, consumed by grief, angst and drinking myself to death.

The sky is dark. The sky is deep. The sky is rich. It settles low. I feel it smother and surround me as I leave my house. My feet squelch and skid on the sodden leaves and litter. Branches bash one another like conkers competing in a cup final. Jets of rain bounce off grubby leaves as people huddle under trees and bus stops, jostling side by side to avoid the driving drops. I struggle to find a seat and stand on a cramped commuter train to the horror that is Canary

Wharf. I sit on an uncomfortable train in an uncomfortable suit to spend my day sat in an uncomfortable chair having uncomfortable conversations.

The train stutters and chokes with an undercurrent of sadness and sorrow, transporting cattle from their loved ones and warm beds. The polyester suits shuffle around one another as the train trickles to a shuddering stop. My stop, Canary Wharf, located 250 metres from my office. I look around at the racing rats and ponder the point of it all. The longer we live, the further from our dreams we fall and further into the abyss. The dreams we have as children fade away. I started working here two years ago in March.

It wasn't what I wanted to do, but it wasn't so bad. A stopgap, a temporary measure, a short, sharp stop zone. The first few months flew by. The first week acquiring stationery, taking care of the endless coffee runs and working out who is sleeping with whom. The ghastly gossiping and childish Chinese whispers. Weeks turn to months and before you know it you have your feet under the table. People now come to you asking where various files are stored on the company server and how to operate the microwave. There is then there's talk of promotion, a pay rise and a pension. You are stuck. Your mind is warped, and you are trapped like a small fly in a large web.

The slowness of my day drills away, slowly but surely hammering away. It beats, it bangs. My eyes are constantly drawn back to the view from my window. I long for release. I look around at my bored-stiff colleagues and wonder what we did wrong to end up here. A class of faces frozen in dullness, lost forever in a cauldron of just making do. The rain continues to beat against the window. As afternoon turns to evening, clouds turn to rain and my expression turns to desperation.

It's late evening and I get off the tube. Walking to my flat I pass group after group of bored Bengali teenagers. On the other side of the road white English working-class rude boys eye up their opposition. I keep my gaze fixed to the floor. Every other shop has ceased trading. Somers Town, a waste ground of sorrow, struggle and hardship. Young men with slick haircuts wolf whistle as teenage girls in vast amounts of make-up clatter past in high heels they are barely able to stand in.

Dark bruising grey consumes the drab city skyline. What little light remains is lifeless. A chilly drizzle consumes the evening air, the whistling wind biting all in her path. The evening is silent. Approaching the off licence, I feel a twitch and am already giddy in anticipation of being drunk. I don't have many friends or family. After a long day I find comfort in alcohol. I drink alone. Since losing Daisy I avoid people. I don't enjoy the taste, but alcohol has become my best friend of late. I drink to fumigate the demons using alcohol as my coping strategy. Alcohol helps to blanket my angst and cope with everything going on in my head; it prevents me from feeling quite so lonely.

I check my wallet. I have nine pounds, so purchase two bottles of red wine. I try to recall the last time I was in a good mood, the last time I felt anything that resembled happiness or excitement, and fail miserably to picture a single scene. Returning home, I climb the stairs, avoiding the hoodlums sat on graffitied steps, nodding in unison as hip-hop beats from their smartphones serenade their cannabis-addled heads, and African beats blare from my next-door neighbour, piercing the evening peace.

I sit and stare from my wobbly, weeping window as my final cigarette reduces to a wet butt. In the flat opposite loud, lairy lovers spit venom and wave their hands furiously at one another. Below them, a balding man in a string vest leans from a bathroom window and spits a mouthful of toothpaste on the floor below him. A tatty St George's flag flutters from the Sky dish above him. The traffic fades. I finish both bottles of wine and feel relief as it numbs my racing mind. A calmness washes over me, pushing me into a comatose transient state of bliss. A stone's throw away from my view a young couple are locked in a kiss. I fantasise that I, one day, will be with a lover at a bus station, locked in arms, locked in thoughts and locked in looks.

January 13th

The morning weather is vicious. Lightning bolts dagger motionless groups of clouds, waking them into life. Spits of rain bounce like Mexican jumping beans across my thin glass pane. The curtains beside me have visible mould forming on them; the ceiling above is caked in nicotine. Outside, angry barking canines drag their tracksuit-wearing owners at breakneck speed. Rastafarians in brightly coloured baseball caps with loud logos on tight-fitting jumpers knock knuckles, exchanging small bags for cash. The time is just after eight, with folk already up to no good.

My view, a brutal and sad social landscape. The car park opposite is polluted with beer cans, bottles, bog rolls and bin bags. Skinny cats hiss aggressively at pot-bellied dogs.

Moody grey clouds consume the horizon above me, restricting the slightest beam of sunlight from entering my day. I pick up my heavy handbag, weighing down one of my skinny, scarred arms. I open my cupboard and pull out a black bomber jacket, a grey T-shirt too large for me and some black denim jeans. My clothes look like they are due some time off.

I look outside as my city awakes. I love London. The hustle, the bustle, the traffic, the tramps. The success and squalor living side by side, the animosity, and the fear. London excites me; it keeps me on my toes. I remember when I first moved to London. It will be eight years ago next week. I felt excitement, excitement like I could burst. Somers Town, a small suburban enclave in north central London, sandwiched between Camden Town and Kings Cross with little going on. I felt invisible and, in a peculiar way, safe, lost and unseen in urban deprivation and isolation.

London had hold of me. I felt enchanted and enthralled; it was also where I met Daisy. From the second I met her; I knew we would be friends for life. It was in the toilets of the Dolphin pub one Friday night where our paths crossed and our friendship commenced, Daisy ferociously doing her hair and plastering make-up on her pasty face. Her pupils dilated like dinner plates; her hands shook. I asked if she was OK. She smiled and asked where I'd purchased my racing-green parka. I then joined her and her party for a rum cocktail. The next thing it was Monday morning, both of us sat in her front room until the last of the Rizlas had been rolled and the final record had been spun. We didn't need any money, just each other, our thoughts and our passions. We would listen to records, dance to our heroes and talk until our tongues ran dry. But then I lost her.

The day has started but life wakes slowly. Empty buses pass infrequently and on litter-filled streets, more pavement than people is visible. Shutters on corner shops open, but passing trade is minor. The sky transforms colour as dark, dreary damp is replaced by crystal-clear skies. The morning sun flares, fighting its way past factory rooftops, pushing and peering past tatty tower blocks.

I arrive at the canal and sit down on the bench we once shared. I light a cigarette and gaze across the water's edge, taking a deep drag and then exhaling. The morning sun is creeping. It bounces off the brittle brickwork opposite and reflects back into my tired eyes. Small sparkles dance and dive in the water around us. Tiny fragments drift along the narrow canal's edge. The skin of the water gleams and Daisy and I are together again. The world seems suspended. Flocks of bird scatter the skies, flirting and dancing with one another. As I look across the water I am flattened by flashbacks of Daisy. I look at her photo, her elegance and grace like that of a spectacular swan on a luscious lake, and grasp her tightly in my hand, clenching my shaking fist.

I talk and talk but no words come back, our conversation now forever a one-way street. We sit in silence as my thoughts are the only noise I hear. I feel as if I have been punched and let out a howl. Grief exhausts and beats me. I am sinking, swallowed deep into a dark unforgiving sea, drifting, drowning, swirling and suffocating. I am weak and powerless, my words muffled and my muddled mind waterlogged.

I feel myself wheezing as panic, terror and tremors hit me. Grief's fixed stance looms large and laughs at me; its cruelty knows no bounds. I am dazed and disoriented as a deep sadness sours my everywhere. I am lost, vulnerable and frozen. Swirling images of Daisy and her passing cloud my thoughts. My breathing turns shallow and my hollow heart races. I am in a hole. A deep, dark hole. One I no longer have the desire or fight to clamber out from. I am on the brink. I lay my head in my hands and the tears return, this time running down my nose and down the nape of my neck. There is a wave of hurt in my stomach; it contracts and constricts.

Beside me on the floor is a glass bottle with sharp, frayed edges. I take the edge of my coat and clean the end of the bottle. My heart races. I close my eyes and then push the sharp ends deep into my left wrist. I scream. My hands are now covered in blood. Thick, rich, oozing blood. I twist the bottle and the blood runs faster; it makes me feel alive. The voices and noise within my mind cease. My teeth chatter, though the temperature's not low. I feel warm inside as an electric glow gathers over me. I continue to twist the glass. It calms and smoothers me.

For the first time in what seems like an eternity I feel I have some form of control over my emotions. The power swings to my side of the court. Even if just for this moment, the pendulum has swung, and the power is mine. The blood keeps running; the power is mine. I twist the bottle further, taking revenge on my grief, and feel the surge sweep me off my feet and away; the power is mine.

Smashing glass abruptly wakes me from my sleep. I am late for work. The alarm sound progressively grows louder, intensifying and aching my ears. My eyes dart at the time in a furious fashion. I continue to arise at an outrageous hour to an unbearable alarm. Rancid red wine buckles and bites the back of my throat as I stretch for the aspirin tablets ideally located on the bedside table. My head screams. I am frantic and frail and pant like a hot puppy locked in a car on a scorching summer's day and taste my stale boozy breath.

Morning breaks, birds sing and commuter trains creak. A thin fog hovers, slowly lifting and revealing London's vast city sky. The city's sirens and sounds drifting in and out of my dreams. My insides are shattered and broken. My mind is dusty; dark spaces consume my mind. I hide my recent self-harm with bandages. An urge of disgust sweeps through me. I am anxious, irate and panic-stricken. I sit on the windowsill, aimlessly gazing at a kaleidoscope of towers and trees before me in the streets and alleys afar.

It rains. The rain is hard and ferocious, causing me to tremble like a leaf in a unrelentless storm. Blanket after blanket of water batter shop windows as drains overflow, full to capacity. Diagonal sheets continue to fall. It is early. Pylons wobble and flocks of birds appear to fly backwards. I pass prison-like accommodation. There is a double mattress with its insides gouged out beside a lonesome television with its face smashed into fragments. A man approaches. I smell him before I see him. He is old with bruises all over his face. Grey frizzy hair explodes from his saggy ears. Old creases consume the worn-out, saggy, reptile-like skin that hangs heavy from his neck. His eyes bulge from their sockets. He is shouting at me, at everyone. I pay no mind, keeping my eyes fixated on the floor.

Gaggles of teenage boys glare from walkways above, resting their skinny elbows on cold, hard, concrete balustrades, spitting on the floor in unison like fine musicians being conducted at a philharmonic orchestra. On cold, cobbled street corners folk lean against stationary rubbish bins stacked to the rafters, smoking their lives away. I run to the bus stop over grassless, cracked mud football pitches.

I pause briefly to light a cigarette and shield the weather from me with the thin, dark cotton lining of my jacket. Puddles grow, city parks swamp. Cold hands in wet pockets rattle on my shaking thighs.

The office canteen has just opened. I order a strong coffee. Opposite me, bored businessmen play with their phones. I look at one guy and long for him to notice me. I look into my cracked mirror, furiously wiping the sleep from my eyes, and quickly re-apply my make-up. A stray hair catches my mouth. He looks at me for a few seconds, momentarily catching my gaze, but then I lose him as his eyes revert their attention to a girl much younger than I, with rich auburn curls and ample cleavage, at the table to his right. He looks at her long enough to make her quite clear of his intention should she be interested. His eyes then drift back to his smartphone, eager to find love in the fastest way possible, ferociously swiping left and right. Outside on the other side of the window the world moves slowly. The sky is pale like snow.

I spend my day in and out of meetings, staring at blank screens, chasing leads, going through the motions and sending arbitrary emails to hide my heartache and grief, hoping the faster I tap my keyboard the further from my thoughts Daisy will be. It doesn't work; instead the mundane tasks of my day are merely magnified. Losing Daisy has made me realise I had lost sight of what my life was meant to be. It's made me question everything. Daisy's passing has given perspective and made me realise how I should be spending my time. I spend the afternoon re-evaluating everything, working out where I am meant to be.

The reactions from my colleagues have been varied: some act as though nothing has happened; some ask morbidly curious questions. Folk are more stand-offish; people that once engaged in complex conversations now keep me at arm's length, nervous and frightened of saying the wrong thing, afraid to make eye contact, and not knowing what to say. Friends with whom I would often discuss weekend shenanigans with now offer a nervous wave. I have little appetite. I have begun carrying blades in my purse and now self-harm in the workplace. When feeling grey, empty and weak, I go to the bathroom. It wakes me from my anguish. The compulsion of indulging in my self-harm is too powerful to fight. The pain and release create a focus for my thoughts, shifting me out of my mundane existence and offering me ownership over my body.

I am overwhelmed and my mind is foggy. I just want to feel normal again. I often receive a reminder when I am least expecting it, causing me to run to the toilet and cry, cut, shrink and vomit. It could be a Kings of Leon song on the office playlist or a colleague passing in a Topshop top Daisy once wore. It could even be her favourite sandwich filling on the canteen's specials board. I return home most evenings surprised I've made it through my day. I feel robotic and uncertain, guilt-ridden, saddened and remorseful that I am still here, and she is not. I rarely talk to people in the office these days. I keep myself to myself, pretending I'm fine in front of others, acting normal, acting strong.

Leaving the office, the evening is vocal; it sings to me. It rains; moisture hangs heavy in the air as clouds knock together like crowded commuters, covering the slightest trace of blue. I walk the long way to the shop to ensure I spend less time at home. My body drifts with the wind as I aimlessly float back and forth, anything to be at home alone. Once home I drink until I am numb and stare out the window, my gaze picking out people. A solitary, orange streetlamp illuminates the evening. I watch until the night becomes slow motion and begin to surrender myself to sleep. My body drifts in and out of consciousness as the noise inside my mind becomes louder, droning out car engines and emergency sirens.

January 29th

A bereavement support group is a group I had never envisaged being a part of. I accept I need help, though. The advert in the local paper states that the group is a place where atmosphere and the personalities are kind and supportive.

I call the number and the phone rings repeatedly. Just as I am about to hang up, someone answers. It is the voice of a lady with a Geordie accent. She sounds sincere and has a soft voice with a caring tone. Her name is Julie, and she tells me I would be very welcome to attend. She asks what made me call. I spend ten minutes talking to her about Daisy. I tell her I am struggling and broken. She tells me the group takes place at her house on Camden Park Road, that it is weekly and I'm welcome to attend this evening. It couldn't do any harm. I couldn't feel any worse. Feeling slow and sad has become my new normal. I don't want to waste any more time. I need to try and fix what's broken, shift the darkness and recreate the light that used to beam within. Grief holds no beauty. If I am going to get better, I need to understand my grief.

The rush-hour traffic is relentless. I am late; I hate being late. Irate drivers with glum commuter frowns grunt as vehicles grind to a halt and appear almost glued together. I check the house number against what is saved in my mobile phone and ring the doorbell for the second time. I run my fingers through my hair, impatiently waiting at the door, then in a flash it opens.

"Ada, right? Julie told me you were coming. I am Vincent, most people call me Vinnie, pleased to meet you." He has a shaven head, thick beard and striking green eyes.

I meet Julie, whom I spoke to on the phone, the group founder. Vinnie guides me to a seat in the front room and introduces me to everyone.

When everyone is seated, the talking stops and Vinnie stands. "My daughter Sophie was six years old when I lost her. It was car accident. A drunk driver came head-on the other way. I tried to move out the way but couldn't; it all happened so fast. It was just me and her in the car. She died and I survived. Upon waking in hospital, I was told Sophie hadn't survived.

"I wanted to make Sophie proud and thought perhaps coming here going might give me an opportunity to help others. As rough as I feel, I'm sure there will be someone feeling just as bad. From a selfish perspective, if I can guide and support someone else in their struggle with grief then perhaps it might help me sleep better at night too.

"I find peace and solace in coming here. I am able to reflect, with time and space to breathe to help heal my mind and my soul. I find hope and healing, clarity and focus. Being here quietens the noises in my head when the day-to-day becomes too severe and my racing mind aches. I find it almost therapeutic. Some days whilst I'm here, I lose my words and am unsure quite what to say, but I'm OK with that and just hope Sophie is too.

"There were so many things we had planned to do that we keep putting off and then it was too late. Nothing prepares you for it. I felt so hopeless and hollow. I am left with this permeant ache that is now part of my life; however, gradually I'm learning to live with this. I still have hard days but feel better than I did a few months ago. I feel more like the person I am capable of being and like I have turned a corner.

"My loss is no stronger than anyone else's. I am not stronger for my grief. I long for my old life. I long for that spark, that something, anything, that little burst of brilliance where, for just a moment, my world feels wonderful. But moments like that have abandoned me. I want to surround myself with people who understand how I'm feeling – that's why I came here. If I can help any of you then please let me know." Vinnie stops speaking and smiles.

Everyone in the room claps and smiles back.

Julie asks if I would like to talk.

"Hi, erm… I'm Ada. I'm sorry, I haven't prepared anything. I haven't written anything," I respond nervously.

"It's fine, love, maybe next time," says Julie in a sympathetic tone.

"No, no, it's fine. I would like to. I think. I mean, yes, if that's OK," I say. "OK… The reason I'm here is because of Daisy. Daisy was my best friend, my only true friend. She was everything and more that you could wish for from a friend. She was warm, generous and great fun. She wasn't one for taking life too seriously. She was so full of life and laughter and would light up any room.

"Daisy had fibrous cysts in her breast. The lumps she discovered wouldn't go away. A biopsy revealed it was cancer. She was told her odds of surviving the rest of the year were fifty-fifty. The chemotherapy was tough. It was like using a baseball bat to squash a pea. It was overpowering but had to happen. She needed to feel better; she needed fixing. She took on the battle, but she lost. Daisy didn't win and I lost my best friend."

Tears run down my cheeks. I stop talking and bite at my ketchup-red chipped painted nails. My heart races. I try to continue and open my mouth, but my words are lost and won't come out. The tears fall faster and my voice breaks.

I get up and run to the front door as the volume inside my head levitates. My insides scream. I leave the house and start running as fast as I can. I shake. I cry. I run. Bus drivers bang their windows and beep their horns in a furious fashion as they narrowly avoid me jumping in their path. I am unsettled and overwhelmed, unsure of what to do next. Fear takes complete control. I flag down a taxi to the only place I know, the canal. I look for Daisy. I tell her about the group and how stupid I must have looked. I wait for her to tell me it's OK. She fails to respond, as she always will.

February

Ollie

There is not a cloud in sight, but not the faintest hope of sunshine either. Dark skies loom ominously. Slowly, we walk to the back garden, then further still, down a winding narrow path. Grace takes my hand. The hard soil turns my toes cold. It's quiet but for the noise of our feet foraging formations in soggy, limp, withered leaves. After a few minutes the bundle of leaves we traipse through turn to stone, leading us to a small pond and narrow bench. Cold morning air bounces off the thin sheet of ice delicately lacing the water's surface. As we take a seat, she looks at me; her gaze momentarily melts my melancholy. Tears run the length of her cold, creased cheeks.

"I love you. I'm sorry."

Her words a limp whisper through wobbling, thin, broken lips. Her tears keep falling as the lump in my throat largens. She wears a tired portrait and looks like she has been up for days. All light falls from her eyes. Wicked, black circles hang horridly beneath her once beautiful shining eyes. Our sadness and pain collide, crash and crush one another. Our heavenly existence is vandalised and violated as our world's ripped apart at the seams.

Death is here. He lurks. He is upon us and present, but I won't let him have her, not yet. I close my eyes and see him in all his wickedness. I shut my eyes, but the vision is still there. I shut them tight. Still he dances around us, lingering and waiting, impatient to take Grace from my desperate grasp. I lift her into bed. She is weightless in my arms. She clamps my shaking, sweaty hand in hope of reassurance and begins to break. Observing her self-destruction causes makes me break. She whimpers and wails, struggling with each breath, slowly but surely falling to pieces. Her expression is so lost in grief it would take a pair of pliers to make her smile. I turn away and sob so hard I am barely able to breathe.

Time slips away; the ticking clock is close to stopping as the battle we hoped to win falls further from our hands. We stand together but stand small, united in defeat. Tears fill my eyes; the harder I try to stop them, the faster they fall. I am helpless and lost. I feel a fraudster and failure for promising Grace the world, a world, soon to be shut down, detonated and destroyed.

I catch a glimpse of her reflection in the windowpane, a glimpse of death. All the talk of hope, strength and luck; it all comes down to fate. The wonder of life halts as her beautiful human heart slows. I hold her and feel her war. The stars that once beamed and sparkled between us dissolve, disintegrate and dim. She closes her eyes and drifts in and out of sleep. Her knees knock together and tremble. I rest her hands on my chest. I hold them and cease their shaking. *Grace, let me take your hand and guide you to somewhere safe. Let us float away and glide above in perfect powdered clouds and not look back.*

She is now in my arms as her head limply rests on my shoulder. She whimpers and wails. I try to calm her. "It's OK," I softly whisper in her ear. I turn my face the other way from hers and gaze at the tainted, salmon-coloured wallpaper. The pair of us are crushed and crumbled in knowledge that my words are false. I feel guilt. Guilt that she is feeling pain that I'm not experiencing. Guilt that she will die, and I will survive. Guilt that she gave me everything and in return I have given her nothing.

"I'm so sorry. I wish I could have protected you. I should have protected you. I found you. I can't lose you. Don't go, Grace."

She tells me she is sorry too. Her words leave a vulgar void in my heart. Our lips meet and I taste her pain. My lips tingle. A film of oily sweat runs the length of my face. She looks at me, agitated and afraid. I feel I am standing on the sky's edge, narrowly balanced and nervous, anticipating the hell that awaits me, awaits us. I wish I was brave. I wish I was strong. I bite my nails in a furious fashion, attack after attack at each sorry stub. She looks up towards me. She is lost. She is leaving. I try to refrain from morbid, remorseful thoughts as I squeeze her hand. The tears come. She reaches out and looks at me, pleading for me to help. Her existence is the only sense the world has ever made. The chamber of my heart rattles and rings.

Grace attempts to stand, but the pain is too intense. She starts to howl. I sob so hard my whole body shakes. This is the end. She has little time left but my thoughts are not regret or remorse, instead pride and joy. Pride that Grace remained positive and always held her head high.

Grace smiles and everything stops. She smiles and all evil is washed away, replaced with a rich, warm wave that sweeps over us both. Her beautiful face has grown pale, but she manages one final smile. She closes her eyes and I scream. I plead and beg for them to open, but she is gone. My world stops. My feeling of completeness is washed away and replaced with emptiness. My stomach churns. Excited butterflies that once danced lie dormant. She is gone. I feel faint. My heart breaks. Busy nurses buzz around me. Unrecognisable voices bellow and scream. I get lost in the noise. I am on top of her and I am losing her.

"Don't go, Grace, don't go. Please, Grace, please."

A bleak sheet casts a shadow, consuming my view. There is no colour as all light departs. The tears come in waves; they multiply and won't cease. I am now on my knees and unable to stand. Anger flares and raises his tormented head. He washes over all of me. I punch the floor. I try to walk, but it's impossible. I struggle. I stumble. I fall; each step is more painful than the last. Sharp pains bite me. Freezing cold, stabbing daggers dig all over. There is no specific area; it is everywhere. They hurtle towards and flatten me.

She is immobilised, but she is leaving. I am unable to block her departure. I scream but not a single word is able to voice the hurt inside me or cease the inevitable. Everything is twisted and torn. My racing heart beats. I wish I could give it to her. I wish so dearly I could replace her broken body with mine. My arms and legs uncontrollably shake. She slowly slips away to the deepest of sleeps, the eternal sleep. I am unable to wake her. I kiss her. I taste her death and cry. I stroke her pitch-black eyebrows and dry lips for one last time.

She is calm and still, quiet and at peace. I am alone terrified and anxious. My loneliness is so vast it covers me whole. It swamps me; my breathing becomes irregular. A noose around my neck grapples me and tightens. A face that I fail to recognise tells me it's going to be OK. I bite my tongue and swallow my venom.

I sob so hard, I collapse. I am in and out of consciousness.

I lie on the floor, warped with fear, and weep like a newborn baby. I sob so hard my whole body shakes. The cold floor slaps each time I struggle. I feel a deep burning anger and resentment for everyone else alive. I want the world to sense a communication with me and my loss. I want to be held. For people to reach out, touch me and tell me this is not really happening.

I am boiling hot then freezing cold and clench my fists. She has gone, so has all colour; only dark remains. I beg for heavy, horrid storms to suck and swallow me complete.

My mind is desperate, desolate, and my insides ring. A parade of pins and needles scorns my skin. I am broken and bruised; my landscape is bleak and dim. A deep, sour depression circulates around me. My sadness soars. A sadness not just circumstantial, for this sadness is for keeps. I am entirely and utterly alone. I am anxious, empty, abandoned, paralysed and punctured. I am certain of nothing but unsure of everything. My world's turned on its head. The carpet is pulled beneath my feet as I slide away on a raft of angst.

Raging voices from the flat above break my sleep. Car ignitions spit and choke as the school run starts. Yummy mummies squeeze screaming kids inside sleek saloons and city gents with toast still in hand quickly clamber to their company car to avoid the morning rush. The beat of heels tap quicker and quicker, folk on their way to where they need to be.

I wake on my bedroom floor fully clothed, momentarily wondering where I am. I wonder where she is too. I am tearful for my favourite part of the day that has now passed, that moment when I wake each morning unable to differentiate between dreams and reality, where I return to the man I once was. A thirsty flower flops its weary face on the windowsill beside me. When Grace died our plants died too.

Bright, beaming orange cuts through the morning sky as blemishes of sun flicker through my wood-slated blinds. Bright light glimmers into my eyes as shreds of light show themselves amongst speedy, hurrying clouds. In the distance the birds sing a melodic but mournful song to break the morning muteness.

My head is a kaleidoscope of chaos and catastrophe. I never imagined finding love, but with Grace I did. I would spend a lifetime alone to share just one more minute in her company. Grace patched the hole in my heart and made my insecurities cease. Her beauty blurred my vision. She was my reason for living, my safety haven and shelter. She absorbed my entire existence, providing a sanctuary for my soul. She made my insides fizzle and pop and the pit of my stomach tingle and twist.

I feel anxious and exhausted. An exhaustion no rest will cure. The emptiness I feel is indescribable as unwelcome voices murmur in my vacant mind. The voices get louder, deafening me, clattering and clunking; wicked thoughts rage, reverberate and suffocate me. There is a knock at the door. I open it; no one is there. On the doormat sits a beautiful bouquet of flowers. The pretty pastel colours startle me. On the top is a card. "Ollie, I'm so sorry for your loss, take as much time as you need, we are all thinking of you. Ben and the team XX."

I pass the fridge and look at the photo of me and Grace. We are on Brighton beach and the sun is coming down. Grace is carrying a large cocktail glass, too heavy for her hand. The pier is behind us and I wear a stupid, carefree grin. Grace loved this picture. I stare at the picture and sob. I feel a rage within me. I pull the picture from the fridge and tear it in two.

Frustration, resentment and bitterness consume me. I am light-headed, dizzy and frail. My body is weak and my energy stationary. My stomach is empty and my heavy head throbs. Nausea sweeps all of me and I gag. I cough and splutter and am sick. This is how my day begins. Paranoia is persistent and I fear it always will be. Every noise, shadow and silhouette, a potential danger. I am jumpy and forever fearful. My heart is broken. I am shipwrecked, lashed and beaten, alone and laid to waste. I reach for the letter. I read it once. I read it twice. I read it ten times. I sob. I wail.

Dearest Ollie,

I write this letter in anticipation that I shall not see you again. Please don't be sad. Life is too short and far too precious. I remember when we met – you were so full of life, excitement and fun. I fell in love with you instantly. Grief can make us sad, tremble and fall, but true love conquers all. True love is what we had. We were lucky. Many people will live a lifetime not experiencing true love. We had it for four years. Don't allow your grief to shatter the love we shared.

Open your heart to someone else (not just yet! But in time). You deserve to be happy and someone else deserves to feel the happiness and warmth you gave me. I remember our wedding day. It was the most wonderful day of my life; my heart felt as if it would explode. You were all I could have wished for in a husband and more. I believed together we would grow old and become one of those couples invisible to everyone but ourselves. I am so very sorry I won't grow old with you.

I dearly wish I could be by your side forever. Always keep trying. Follow your dreams. Be your best. Be wise, thoughtful, loyal and fair. Never forget the memories formed over our time together.

All my love, forever and always, your wife, Grace
xxxxxx

Empty vodka bottles and ashtrays crammed to capacity litter the living-room floor.

I am embarrassed of my reaction to Grace's passing, aware just how disappointed she would be. I pace the room at speed, gripped by rising panic, feeling guilt and shame at my recklessness. The pain is almost unbearable; my heart races uncontrollably. My thoughts are dark and desperate. My tired body quivers, tortured by hallucinatory waking nightmares. My stomach cramps and churns. I shake and sweat, crippled with anxiety and the realisation of impending doom, and feel myself falling deeper into the abyss.

I remove a bottle of vodka from the freezer. Just holding the cold, hard bottle makes me feel at ease. One more drink and I will be OK. I drink the remaining third of the bottle in a single gulp, with hope of suffocating and swamping my sadness. My world starts to spin, and the bright lights fade. There is no glory or glee. The shaking halts. My rage retracts. The bliss of blackout. Take me away. I lose control and everything becomes slow motion. I lie down and wait for my eyes to roll to the back of my head, filling me with unconsciousness. The blackness takes over like a murderous, vile virus. I am suffocated by a mountain of black tar. Darkness. A notion of nothingness. I pass out.

February 25th

Smoke drifts from cooling towers, clouding my city skyline. Block after block of inner-city estates submerge from the misty melon morning sky. The view from my window a collage of colour, as historic North London architecture meets modern-day conversions. The landscape is compact but retains its beauty. Railway tracks rattle in need of repair, carrying commuters clumped together like sardines trapped in a tin.

A crack of light from the morning sun warms my brow. I wake with a pounding head and little recollection of the night before. I am dazed and confused. I feel anger, sorrow and self-hatred. My insides cramp. I am a quivering ball of shame. I feel paranoid and anxious. I talk to myself, panic-stricken; at times I talk to the furniture. Alcohol has become more important to me than the food I seldom eat or the air I unwillingly breathe. I pass out, slumped drunk in front of the television, most evenings and spend each morning recovering. My alcohol dependency feels like a terminal illness. I have reached the point where a sustainable level of alcohol is required to keep my life from collapsing altogether. Feeling slow and sad has become my new normal. I am unable to live without it, irrespective of how much misery and pain I cause myself. I feel my life drifting away. I pour a myself a sizeable measure of warm gin and knock it back in one.

My mind is blank and broken, an empty landscape, a vast, bleak emptiness with no beauty within. My insides are sunken; there is no inner peace. I feel anxiety. I feel hurt. I feel dizziness and my chest tightens. I stand up, but my limbs ache. Outside a thin drizzle has started. I close my eyes and run my finger across the creases in my forehead. I feel restless, strained by my isolation and stressed by my surroundings.

I go to the bathroom and look in the mirror, almost surprised at my self-neglect.

I have aged so very quickly these past few weeks. My hair looks like it is thinning. I notice heavy veins on my forearm I am unable to recall seeing before. They circulate my limbs like wild snakes constricting their prey. I have lost weight. My skin is blotchy and red. My tight, floppy, brown curls are greasy and matted. My grey cardigan looks almost black and my heavy-rimmed glasses in need of a clean. I leave my flat and pass the concierge. She is chewing gum and talking on her mobile phone in broken English. Her ears wiggle. The faster she talks, the faster her lugholes move, as if her lips and ears are engaged in a race.

Murky grey clouds hang heavy above, swallowing the faint remains of light from the morning sky as thin, naked branches dance and glide over one another. I kick piles of brown, crusting leaves and stand powerless, watching as the world goes by in slow motion; I gaze aimlessly at passers-by and morning commuters and do my best to melt into their core. The sadness, the sorrow and grief hang heavy on my shoulders as I try my best to lose myself in London's anonymous streets. My bones ache and my head hurts. I am envious of everyone with somewhere to go and somewhere to be. I so dearly wish I had somewhere to be. I feel the morning sky loom large. I feel it get bigger and bigger; it dwarfs me, making me feel insignificant.

Heat rises within me. This feeling overtakes me, drifting me away from where I stand. I walk into my local café and try to read the paper but am unable to concentrate. I drink a coffee. I drink another coffee. I detest these dismal days. The dullness thuds my insides and eats away at me, leaving me lost and alone. It echoes around me, sucking at my overworked and absent mind. My worries and woes burrow and weave, attacking and assaulting my insides. I am broken and barely able to breathe.

The floors are wooden and the walls covered in paintings. I sit next to a picture of a house. The house is by the sea. I see seagulls, deckchairs and a beach. I imagine I am there, with Grace, sitting inside the house. This is a place where I would like to be, a place where we could be alone, our only companion the bright, blistering sunlight and cool, calm sea.

It looks like Margate, but I can't be sure. It doesn't matter where it is; it could be anywhere. Looking at the waves calms me. I close my eyes and I hear the rhythmic sound of the tide crashing back and forth against the narrow pebbled bay. The sea sparkles and I imagine I am there as my mind momentarily shifts to a calmer state. A tired-looking teenage waitress whizzes past groggy, starry-eyed construction workers and twenty-four-hour party people, almost throwing me my drink. I smile, taking the piping-hot mug from the heavy-handed waitress.

A wasp buzzes against the windowpane. It breaks my concentration, my thoughts muddled and confused. My hangover kicks in. I feel its force. I feel sick. Still the wasp taps on the pane, its angry, tiny black legs kicking out. Outside a storm is brewing. I stare at the roadsides: broken bottles and crushed cans line the pavement. I roll up the paper beside me and, with a short, sharp stab, I squash the wasp, leaving a sickly mess, trying to keep my mind focused on the day that lies ahead.

I walk past an array of overpriced local shops. I live in a part of Holloway so very hollow. A postcode down on its luck, with violence as likely at eight in the morning as eight at night. Music beats behind cardboard windows. Displaced souls scream in my face. Unkempt, grubby misfits reeking of alcohol scream obscenities in my direction. Wreck-heads, winos and wasters wolf down their first meal of the day with more pace than their shaking hands can handle as baked beans dance down the dimples of their chin as their tatty T-shirts and tangled beards end up with more food than their mouth.

Outside the shop the distressing sight of tough and fearless, energetic youths greets me. The gang, decked head to toe in expensive sportswear, down energy drinks at breakneck speed and stare at me. I feel their stares all over me like packs of ants biting at my flesh. Two of them fight. One hits the other. I feel nervous, on edge and concerned, but thankful I am no longer the focus of their attention.

Returning from the shop I unpack the contents onto the kitchen table. Vodka, bread, cheese and milk. *At least I am safe*, I tell myself. I pour myself a large vodka with no mixer. I down it and it burns. I get back into bed and pull the bedsheets over my head to escape from the world. Life is very long when you're lonely.

March

Ollie

In the distance, church bells ring, causing me to stir. Architecture springs to life as pastel shades brighten the landscape, replacing bleak skies as bright, yellow sunshine marginally brightens my room. It is bright but not warm as wet, cold, heavy air is replaced with flickers of spring. Colours of a change in season began to show themselves and the sky is a brighter sight than a fortnight ago.

Morning birds tweet. I close my eyes. I wish I were a bird and able to fly away from my situation, but my wings are broken, and my insides crushed to pieces. I weep as my body is reduced to a rack of niggling nerves. My brown leather brogues resemble a Jackson Pollock painting with speckles of blood splattered over each worn, tatty shoe. I stare motionless at the outside world as content middle-class couples canoodle. A sharp silence surrounds me as paranoia and fear grow like wild plants within.

I open a can of strong lager and curse as a gaggle of bubbles spit and spray, covering my musty bedsheet. I drink the can quickly. I drink it almost whole. My throat rings. I try to recall falling asleep, but the night before is a blur, just like the one before that and the one before that. On the cabinet next to me is a leaflet I remember being handed a few days after Grace passed. I was informed reaching out to a grief support class could help. I feel I need this help and knowing this eases my anxiety insomuch as I realise I am suffering and can't do this alone. I'm struggling and need something, anything to halt my hopelessness. I am not improving; I am falling and am in full-on narcissistic, self-destruct mode.

I call the number then put the phone down. This happens a further three times. I have another drink, then on the fourth time, I let the phone ring until a softly spoken female answers in an accent I am unable to recognise, my crackling voice almost disappointed the call has been answered.

Her name is Julie and she asks me what made me call. I tell her about Grace. I tell her I am struggling and that I need help, that I am lost and feel unable to last. Something switches within me and everything spills out in all its gruesome glory. I tell her I am breaking, that inside my terror comes in waves and no longer am I able to cope. She talks of her support group and tells me I'm not alone, that I could learn from the experiences of others, finding hope and strength in their support, and tells me to come along this evening. Through my tears and wheezing vocals, I tell her I will try my best to attend.

It is rush hour and folk move at speed for the first available shelter to protect themselves from the vicious, unforgiving, driving rain, hurrying down narrow streets as I attempt to avoid the hustle and bustle of the commuter crush. The wet drizzle makes my tight clothes stick to my cold skin. I use my jacket as a shield to protect me from the driving wind and rain as I wait impatiently for the bus. As I take my seat, I worry what type of person attends a support group. I worry I will be disheartened in the presence of someone else's emotions. Dealing with my own anger, sadness, regret and guilt is troublesome enough; why would I want to listen to and divulge in someone else's grief too?

Arriving at the door my hands clam up. My body shakes as thunderous nerves take over. The door opens and she catches me on the hop. I look her up and down from the pink rose in her hair to the tatty converse that house her small feet.

"Hi, I'm Ada, come in," she says in a calming tone as my anxiety subsides. Her pale, oval, fair face smiles at me and the tiny sparrows centred on her earlobe sparkle. She has light blue eyes almost too big for her face.

Julie, the group leader, then comes forth, shaking my hand. "You made it, Ollie," she says enthusiastically as she takes my shaking, sweating hands and leads me to the front room. She has brown hair that is curly and fine and curious green eyes.

I sit down next to Ada in a half circle. In front of us Julie stands.

"I'd like to start this evening by saying we have someone new to the group – his name is Ollie; I am sure you will all make him feel very welcome."

The whole room looks at me as I feel a rush of discomfort wash over me. The faces look friendly enough, but my embarrassment grows, my insides burn and face glows red.

"To live with grief, we must first understand it. There comes a time in bereavement when we should no longer let it dictate us. By accepting our grief, we diminish its power. We need to remove our hurt to allow us to be free. The purpose of what we are doing is to provide a platform where we can be open and honest and give each other time to talk to digest our grief and offer support to one another.

"Grief at times can feel so very lonely and isolating. By sharing our experiences, fears and feelings the hope is together we can make the grieving process easier for us all. The human spirt is a powerful one and can provide hope and reassurance to those new to grief. Having all been through the trauma of loss it's imperative we work together and find new ways to heal. We will have bad days, but if as a collective we help reduce these then that must be a positive. Let's work together and show that it's possible to feel joy again."

Julie looks at me. "Ollie, would you like to talk?"

My teeth chatter and my mouth is dry. I look around the room at the smiling faces in fear, urging me to talk. Reluctantly I stand, then somehow find my words and talk. "Hello, I'm Ollie, I lost my wife. Her name was Grace. It was cancer.

"Grace had beaten it once and were both confident she would be victorious once more. We became complacent, taking for granted that she would defeat it again. Standing here now I still feel so naïve. People make so many assumptions, just like we did. We were just normal people and didn't want for much. It didn't feel real. Stuff like this happened to other people. I feel so stupid now for believing me and Grace would grow old together; she was just a child, really, when her journey ended.

"The cancer had spread. The nurses kept telling us that they were doing all they could and that she was in the best place possible, but she wasn't. She was in the most awful place she had ever stepped foot in. She looked so angelic laid there in her bed as if she were just sleeping and waiting for an alarm to wake her.

"I sat in her room with her and we just stared. We held hands and gazed aimlessly at each other for hours with seldom words spoken. Her critical body systems were beginning to fail. I would look at her with a stupid, hopeful grin etched upon my panic-stricken face. She would try to engage with me, with a desperate, half-paralysed, tired smile back in my direction, but she was going, we both knew; we were both so afraid and angry, yet still we continued to grin, unsure what else to do. I didn't want her last picture of my face to be fear and tears. We didn't say a lot, we didn't have to, as we sat motionless confined in a landscape of sorrow and sadness.

"Her young body had been compromised beyond a point of no return; the treatment had stopped working. I wanted to protect her and to tell her it was OK, but this time something felt different. I desperately prayed for the whole world to stop, to cease her departure. I wanted to take her and run away together from everything. I promised her that should she ever lose her battle that when they came to take her away, I wouldn't let them, but I couldn't stop it. Grace fell into a sleep, as she often did, but this time I was unable to wake her. She lost consciousness and slipped away. I sat and waited, prayed, screamed and shrieked, but she left.

"Everything stopped. All that remained was eerie stillness. She wasn't here to hold my hand anymore and I had to face the realisation of her passing. I recall seeing people getting into cars, folks talking on their mobile phones and couples squabbling. I wanted to tell the world to stop for a minute and let everyone appreciate how lucky they are. How life is such a magnificent, underrated, beautiful thing that so many imbeciles take for granted. I wanted to scream in the faces of these dimwits that didn't deserve to still be walking these streets. Grace appreciated life. She was happy and didn't deserve this. The idea she was not ever going to move or talk to me again was totally inconceivable. I had never experienced the loss of someone I loved. I had never even been to a funeral."

Tears fill my eyes; I sit down, surprised and startled from where I found my words, and the room claps. Julie introduces me to Vinnie. He is wearing a big watch, an expensive shirt and looks like he has just had a two-week bathe in the sun. His skin glows. He sounds like Hugh Grant when he talks. He is quintessentially English. His looks and mannerisms demand respect. We shake hands and he tells me he is sorry for my loss. I ask him what made him come here. He tells me he lost his daughter Sophie in a car accident.

"When Sophie passed, I was told I would have good days and bad. It's not true: every day is wretched. Some are better than others, but each one is tough. I didn't want to get over losing Sophie or accept she is gone. I was so angry and upset. I was shattered, shaken and left with a hole so big I had no idea how to begin to fill it. There were days when I stopped caring about my own mortality. The loneliness and emptiness were slowly killing me. I wasn't sure which way to turn, where to go next, and then I heard about this place. Grief leaves a legacy and changes you, but coming here has helped; there is healing in being around others in the same situation."

I walk into the kitchen, where Ada stands alone, impatiently waiting for the sage-coloured, rusting kettle to boil. Her mustard tights, with a burgundy corduroy skirt and tight leather jacket, highlight her skinny frame. Outside the window a streetlamp flickers copper light against the pavement. We go to stand outside in the back garden, but the ghastly weather prevents us from doing so. With the door slightly open we watch as darts of driving water pound against the pebble-dashed exterior.

"I love the rain. I could listen to it all day. It reminds me of when I was young. Me and some mates would bunk off school and everyone would come back to mine. We'd nick tapes from music class, those with special effects on." As she talks her thin lips widen, exposing crooked, stained teeth.

"We would turn the lights in my room off then sit in the dark with the tape in my stereo as loud as it would go. Screaming in unison as thunder, rain and lightning bellowed from the speakers." Her T-shirt catches in her jacket as she talks, revealing a thin tummy and pierced belly button. She frowns with deep concentration as she talks, and looks at me and smiles.

"It's OK, you know; to be nervous, I mean. We are all here for the same reason. I feel fortunate to have found this place. I've only been a few times. It's not a normal situation or a place I thought I would be, or perhaps where I would choose to be, but it is what it is, I guess. When you feel alone sometimes all you need is a friendly face and someone to listen," says Ada as she fiddles with her hair.

She gets up and leaves the kitchen.

I get up to leave as Julie stands in my path. "Thank you for coming, Ollie, I hope it wasn't too intimidating. We are all here to help. I hope to see you next week."

There is so much I would like to say, but my words get lost and all I am able to murmur is, "How long until I feel normal?"

She looks at me, her face tough, but with warm, welcoming eyes, and says nothing and just smiles.

I return home, consumed with guilt for talking to Ada. A sharp rush of panic takes over, twisting my insides. Precariously I balance on the corrugated cast-iron radiator, pulling myself up through the loft hatch above just big enough to take my width, and head to the loft to mine and Grace's box of memories. My throat is dry and hands itch from the fibre glass insulation that surrounds me. Inside the loft the soles of my shoes softly dance from beam to beam, narrowly avoiding the boxes of vinyl records and the artificial Christmas tree before finally I reach the photos.

Inside my mind a wild storm brews; my heart quickens as anxiety rushes through me. I shouldn't have spoken to Ada. What would Grace say? What would Grace think? My hands shake. Frantically I search through the photos for the one of our wedding day. I find the photo, my racing heart slows, and I whisper to her how sorry I am.

March 31st

Barking dogs shatter my sleep. The morning sky burns a beautiful, bright pink.

The trees have turned that beautiful colour again. The air is warm but my body trembles. The darkness fades away and all that was once black and white contracts into a sharp, beaming colour. Shafts of sunshine yellow the leaves of the trees outside my view as screeching trains creep through the fog of my sleep.

I feel tired and slightly nauseous and struggle to wake as my eyelids overpower my mind. I awake with my pillow wet and sticky. I have little reflection of my dreams but remember feeling agitated.

I gaze out my window and stare across the vast, naked skyline in front of me. There are no birds, clouds or planes. The bright sky burns my eyes. London is unusually warm for this time of year. Beaming light pours in through my window, bright enough to blind me. I have a shower and think of Ada. I hate myself. I brush my teeth and think of Ada. I hate myself.

I spend the morning looking at old photos as my mind is paralysed in guilt. I don't want to forget Grace, but I know looking at our past doesn't benefit me. I worry whether I should stop looking at our pictures; perhaps it means I'm moving on and forgetting her. I long for the day where I can view these photos in a positive light and feel joy but worry I never will. I think about this evening's group. I think about Ada and feel disgust for thinking about another female, but going to this evening's group is something to focus on and a deterrent to stop me from drinking.

The evening is closing in as tired workmen still drill on city pavements, their hands and head vibrating from the power of the pneumatic drill. I give the door two knocks and am welcomed by Julie's smile. I sit in Julie's compact but comfy front room and feel relaxed. Vinnie pulls a seat up next to me; he tells me had his own business selling high-end cars for a living.

"I miss it so much. I would love nothing more than to get that pinstripe suit out just one more time. I had it all, but I lost it. For a while everything I touched turned to gold, but when I lost Sophie, everything else followed. I did my utmost to pretend it wasn't happening and hit the self-destruct button. Clients stopped wanting to deal with me. I stopped caring and wanted to damage and destroy myself.

"I stopped working and the money stopped coming in. I couldn't face getting out of bed, let alone making myself presentable. My fleet of cars left my driveway as quickly as they had entered. I was struggling and people found out. Friends stopped calling. It's amazing how differently people view you when your empire is imploding into mush. I just wish I had found this place sooner. I can't describe it; the first day I walked in this room, everything felt OK. When I see these four walls, I feel safe.

"I'm no social butterfly and struggle to let people in, but I feel a connection here. I knew I needed help and it came. I spent the best part of eighteen months contributing to and accelerating my own deterioration. Picking up the pieces of your life and trying to scramble them back together when they have been blitzed into smithereens is hard work."

Vinnie and I play cards; I lose. We play draughts; I lose. We play a game of Scrabble; I lose. He stretches out his strong hand and wishes me better luck next time.

Ada joins us at the table as Vinnie leaves. "Hi, you good?" she asks as our eyes meet. As she waits for my answer, I notice pale freckles that shower the nape of her neck.

"I think so," I say, my concentration momentarily lost as I am drawn into her large and sparkly eyes.

"It will get better, I think," she says as her sharp, spiky cheekbones move whilst she talks.

As she looks at me, I feel a little more alive as particles of darkness are chipped away and the hurt and pain that swoops over me is slightly reduced. I hate myself for feeling like this, but my feelings are impossible to halt. I stare at the floor, feeling guilt for the butterflies that rise within me as she talks. These feelings I find most unwelcoming. I notice cuts on her thin wrists. She looks at me, embarrassed, aware I have seen, and quickly pulls down her tatty cardigan sleeves to cover her wounds.

The front room is now full, and Ada stands; her tired eyes flicker and blink. She looks nervous and embarrassed. She coughs and pauses but is finally able to find her words. "At times my loss feels like it will never leave me. It is always with me, but in some ways, I kind of like it like that, as Daisy is always by my side. At times I feel a fraud for being here when all I lost is a friend. There are people in this room who have lost young children and wives. I feel at times I shouldn't be here, as if my loss doesn't feel large enough, but to me it is.

"I find getting up difficult and going to sleep even harder. Work is a blur. I feel like life is one big act and I'm on stage just going through the motions. I find it hard to cope when small things go wrong and feel more vulnerable to pressures that wouldn't normally affect me. I feel guilt that Daisy isn't here anymore, and I am. Cancer seized her delicate life and shredded it to pieces and all I could do was bear witness.

"Each passing hour of each drawn-out day I feel the need to scream so loud to stop myself from drowning. I feel speechless, lost and alone. I just want to feel like me again. I just want to get back the part of me I admired prior to all this. I'm scared I have lost her forever and that when Daisy died, she died too.

"I feel more unlike myself than I ever have, but when I lose hope I think about Daisy and how cross she would be with me. I imagine her hovering over me as I wallow in self-pity and become so self-obsessed in my own demise. She would no doubt call me 'over-dramatic', as she so often did."

Ada stops talking, with hands deep in her pockets. She looks at me and smiles, her thin lips turning upwards. The time is just after 7pm. I say my goodbyes and leave Julie's house in a furious and sudden storm. The sky is a spectacular tide of seething fury. Rain turns to hail and lashes the stony ground. I find shelter under a tree as stray, twisted branches tangle with my overcoat.

"Ollie, Ollie." I turn around and Ada stands in front of me. "I just wondered; would you like to go for a coffee?" she says nervously in a voice so soft I can barely hear it.

"Er, yes, OK, yes," I say, still and frozen like a statue as I wither in shame. My insides twitch and chest tightens as I feel feelings, I know I shouldn't. My body rattles and rings with a combination of guilt and joy as pins and needles clatter and prang. We sit down in a coffee shop and she talks. She bites her nails and takes deep breaths in between large gulps of coffee. Her thin pale hands shake as she bites her bottom lip.

"I don't know what to do. I just need someone to talk to. I'm so sick of feeling like this." She talks with a croaky throat as tears fill her eyes. Her lungs sound burnt and broken as she heaves and coughs. Her small, pointy chin trembles as she breaks. She looks at me and I look at her. Our eyes dance and dart with one another.

She pushes against me; our lips collide. We kiss. My heart races and my hands shake. I taste her lips. Goosebumps dance along her tiny forearms colliding with mine. My legs and arms tingle; my stomach jumps. It stings. Then it hits me. Panic. I feel a rush of blood to the head. The feeling is intense; I run to the bathroom. I run faster than my shaking legs can carry me. I lock the bathroom door. I slump to the floor and my whole body shakes. I think of Grace, the guilt gathers and the tide is high. It gets darker, stronger, more volatile and fearsome, and it strikes again and now I am drowning. I cough, splutter, hiss and scream, and another wave comes; this time it moves upstream inside me, and I am sick once, twice, three times down cracked and defaced tiled walls.

April

Ada

I hate who I am and what I have become. How foolish was I to dare to dream that I could enhance someone else's existence and that my feelings for Ollie would be reciprocated? Why on earth would anyone want a person like me in their life? I feel myself slipping down a dismal road, deep into a dark hole.

I think about Ollie and how me thrusting myself upon him must have made him feel. I make several desperate attempts to send a text message requesting his forgiveness for my lack of empathy and misreading of the situation. I type then delete, type then delete, and manage just a solitary one-word message: "Sorry."

I think about his wife, his poor wife, and how upset and disgusted he must be with me. I think about what sort of person I am that would intentionally make another human, a sweet person, feel so awkward. This is who I am. If I can work to kill that, even if only to hurt it, I will accomplish my goal. My insides rattle and burn.

I close my eyes. White stars dart around my mind; they circulate, making me giddy. Waves of nausea attack as shame, pain and embarrassment wash over me; it hurts. All of me hurts. Every breath I take I am confronted with confusion and disorientation. My insides are twisted, tangled and torn. I tremble. My hands shake. I rest them on my shaking thighs in hope of ceasing their movement. My racing heart beats faster. I breathe slowly and try to calm myself. Inhale. Exhale.

I open my bedroom window, desperate for fresh air. Outside the sky is gigantic. I feel it get bigger and bigger until I feel so minuscule that there is little left of me and try desperately to refrain from morbid, remorseful thoughts as all power is removed from my grasp. I am veering out of control and my vulnerabilities are now exposed. I am sliding and I crash. I am weak, alone and lost. I wish I was brave. I wish I was strong. The compulsion of indulging in my self-harm is too powerful to fight.

My scissors are new and the blades bright. In a fit of adolescent fury blinded with rage I take my scissors from under my bed and I push them to my skin. Release. Rush. Release. Rush. I look down, shaking, as deep, dark red runs from my limp wrist to the tip of my twitching thumb and feel a thunderous, bellowing rush as the powerful force of blood takes over. I push deeper and it comes; my hurt is deep, sticky, warm and red. I scream as a stillness takes over, for I am free. I have surrendered and given in and now I am free and engrossed in the tranquillity and peace of self-harm. I am deserving of punishment for my wrongdoings and that punishment will come from me.

I hurt, but this route via my skin allows to breathe. My suffocation is diminished, and my inner chaos begins to calm. I find salvation in my own blood. I don't enjoy the process. I feel shame and embarrassment, but my day is now manageable and my anxieties tolerable when I can come back to this. I look around my room. I don't have much, but I will always have this. I have entitlement over me, my skin and my body. I entitled to do what I want to my body, emotionally and physically, as long as I am hurting me and no one else.

It is me now in the driving seat. The clanging and banging from inside my mind halts and a stillness take over. I cut and I am calm. I can lose control of any other situation in my life, but this I can dictate. I cut to make myself free. Tiny pearls of blood dance down my limp wrist and all fog, all anger, dissolves and levitates. A punishment fit for my crime. A gory badge for my bad behaviour. I earnt this. I have numbed my negativity. I am in control.

I bandage myself up and, shame-faced, walk to the canal. There is loud screaming from one of the flats. Aggressive gangster rap rumbles from building to building. The early-morning sun flickers and flares, fighting its way past tower block tops.

I find our bench and sit down. I light a cigarette, the first of the day, and allow the nicotine rush to take over. I look out across the water's edge and talk to my best friend. "I'm sorry." I look down at my bandage as red visible dots begin to bloat the thin cotton and sob, too embarrassed to look up to the water's edge in the knowledge that I have let my friend down.

"You don't need to worry; there is no cause for concern. I'm fine. It won't happen again; it's merely a temporary measure and something to aid my pain when the world feels like it is conspiring against me. I have no intent on hurting myself again, I promise. I just want to stop feeling so sad." I tell her this with a sense of obligation but know my vow will be soon be broken.

My dark thoughts are interrupted by my vibrating phone. It's Ollie. "You have nothing to be sorry for. I'm sorry too." He signs off with a smiley face and a kiss.

April 11th

I awake, disorientated and dishevelled, smeared in my own in my vomit and soaked in sweat and urine. Slowly I lift my head from the floor. I am dehydrated and desperate. The time is 6am. The remains of a drab lasagne ready meal sits beside me. It looks uncomfortable, the slab of greasy carbohydrate too large for the undersized chipped and colourful tea plate it's housed upon. The smell makes me retch. I throw up again. My mouth is dry and my head pounds. Guilt, grief and self-loathing seep from every pore of my trembling body. I slur several words to myself then slowly sink back to the ground.

I stare out the window of my apartment. The sky is bright and clear. I find joy in the layer of padding the alcohol puts between me and the real world. I drink to calm the chaos of my mind. At times I feel I have no choice. Alcohol prevents me from thinking too much. I use alcohol to avoid the questions which race through my mind. Alcohol helps fill the void, the overwhelming sense of emptiness and makes everything very still. It is my dependence. I do not wish to get help. I have control. I am in control.

I stagger to the kitchen and remove a cold, cheap bottle of cava from the fridge. I hold the bottle and feel a glow inside me as I pick nervously at the label and feel a rush of desire. My hands shake in anticipation for the calmness that I know will soon take over. The moment of bliss when stillness takes over the echoes of my mind. The cork pops and the rush of bubbles hits the back of my throat to quench my thirst. The ecstasy of that first gulp is unrivalled as it calms my nerves and put me in a trance. I am transfixed as the warm, cosy blanket of booze suffocates the bleak landscape that lurks behind the void of my racing, frantic mind as I am transported from helplessness to happiness.

Alcohol has always been around me. I grew up in a busy and loving household. My mum and dad owned various pubs in the East End of London. I tasted my first drink aged twelve. It was a glass of mulled wine at Christmas and tasted awful but made me feel relaxed and content. I was a shy child, but alcohol made me feel free and at ease. The euphoria that came with my first drink seemed to make everything OK.

By high school, I was drinking in car parks or abandoned warehouses most weekends. The best numbing agent for teenage angst I found at the bottom of a bottle. Alcohol aided my confidence and helped me talk to boys and befriend girls. When I started university, I got a job at the student union bar. I would always find people to drink with; my drinking and drug intake seemed normal.

On my twenty-first birthday I received a call at work: Mum and Dad had been involved in a car accident. Mum died instantly on impact and Dad was on a life-support machine. A week later I lost Dad too. They were driving back from Devon, where they had been at a family wedding. Dad had been drinking heavily all weekend and hit an oncoming lorry.

After a few dead-end jobs, I finally landed a job in the City. Drinking came with the territory. A few times a week we went out, unwound and bonded over a bottle of wine in a bustling City bar. I would return home and spend the rest of the evening drinking on my own, deep into the night, snorting lines of cocaine to keep me awake to enable me to drink more. Pretty soon drinking with friends lost its appeal. All I wanted to do was lose myself in alcohol and drugs. When Daisy passed my drinking escalated and I gave in to my usual coping strategy. Her absence gives me an excuse to drink. I'm not someone that can have "just a few" and have never understood the logic in opening a bottle of wine without finishing it.

Most evenings I'm drunk and most mornings I awake in a hazy fog. I tell myself it's OK as it blocks my mind and keeps certain thoughts at bay. Oblivion for me is the safest place to be. I drink because I'm anxious. I drink to escape. Alcohol offers a glimmer of hope that life could be tolerable, blocks the thoughts I don't want to feel and momentarily lifts my mood.

In a few hours I am meeting Ollie. Excitement echoes through me but then self-doubt rears its ugly head. My nerves show themselves; my insides jitter and jangle. I have no idea what to wear. After several attempts I decide on a sky-blue shirt with white polka dots, a lilac skirt and my burgundy Doc Martens.

My bright clothes fail to mask my inner feelings. An evil thunderstorm is brewing and breeding. It rattles my bones and churns my insides. I feel I am being infested, gnawed, beaten, suffocated as my skin erodes. I look pale. I feel hollow. I feel weak. My mind won't let me relax or be happy. I beg for the heavy, horrid storms to suck and swallow me complete. Take me away. Take me away.

As much as I wish for Ollie to like me, he won't – look at me. I feel shame, remorse and self-pity. If I am unable to find acceptance in my own skin, how could I possibly expect anyone else to like me? Negative, unmanageable emotions circulate. I drink a large, neat vodka to lower the volume on my anxiety and self-loathing – anything to turn the tide and keep them at bay.

I want to eat; I need to eat. I must feed my empty stomach. I feel odd. I stand up and I am sick. I am sick a further three times. I open my eyes, but it is still dark. Blackness sweeps over and swallows me whole. As much as I'm excited my swilling mind won't let me relax.

I am back on my bed and I reach for the scissors – just touching them makes me felt at ease; I feel a glow burn inside. I push them to my skin and feel the sting. My skin tears and I am on my back and I hallucinate. The darkness fades away and all at once black and white contracts into a sharp, beaming colour.

Images and sounds circulate. Bright, beaming colours. I close my eyes; they are there still. I close my eyes for what seems like an eternity; still they remain. Glorious, luscious, intense, vivid bolts of radiant, rich colours. Open, closed;

open, closed. It makes no difference. Still they remain. I am at peace. Bolts of bronze, vibrant violet and silver slide through my mind. The room spins. I feel pins and needles all over. All over it stings.

A flock of speeding starlings consume the fierce, grey sky above. London's sprawling mess opens before my eyes and no pavement is left untouched as busy feet and bodies collide. Loud voices bellow. I feel weak. I crave some peace, silence, complete and utter stillness. I need to think. I need some peace. The potent aroma of budding flowers mingles in the moist, warm spring air.

I am late and leave my flat at pace, dragging my anxieties with me. I wait for him at the train station next to the car park polluted with Coke cans, bleached by sunlight. The time is just after noon; he is late. I panic that perhaps he won't show at all and then I see a figure; it is Ollie. Waves of emotion pass through me.

We walk to mine and Daisy's bench and take our seat; it is just us, the only noise the raucous quaking of the train as it rattles behind us. I look out at the water. It calms me. A butterfly lands on the space between us. Its turquoise and rose wings flutter at furious speed.

"Daisy, there is someone I want you to meet."

"Hi, Daisy," Ollie says as he waves to the water's edge.

"I wasn't sure you would come; I'm happy you did. I'm sorry about the other day. I didn't mean to offend you – it just happened. I didn't want it to; well, I mean, I did, but… oh God, you know what I mean. I feel daft. I'm sorry."

"Don't be silly, it takes two to tango. I wouldn't I have come had I felt uncomfortable. I have been looking forward to seeing you," he says as he takes a large gulp of coffee.

There is kindness and beauty drenched in his eyes.

He looks at me, at my wrists, and offers a sympathetic stare back in my direction. I am convinced he can smell the alcohol on my breath too.

"You don't have to talk, but if you want to you can. I am here and happy to listen. You aren't alone. There is always another way, a better way. You shouldn't punish yourself. I understand why you do; I feel the same, but you shouldn't."

When Ollie talks, he does so with a calmness that makes my worries float to somewhere else; he makes me feel I am not alone. There is no judgement. Our conversation should be awkward and unnatural; it feels neither. I embrace his warmth and I let him in, exposing my inner secrets and shame. I take a deep breath. I open up and I talk.

"At times my world seems such a fearful place. I feel like I'm waiting for the walls to collapse around me. I never wake planning to do this to myself. Alcohol and self-harm are sometimes the only relief from the intolerable way I feel. I guess it all gets too much. It's hard not to press the self-destruct button when I know where it is. Living alongside my urges and not giving in I find, at times, impossible."

The urge to punish myself for the pain I deserve far outweighs any rational thinking. I deserve to hurt because I am alive, and Daisy isn't. The physical pain I can handle – that's the easy bit, as it masks and distracts from my emotional pain.

"My anxiety elevates to such heights I feel myself ready to snap. It begins with this nagging feeling that clatters and kicks at my insides; there is this devil on my shoulder and he is shouting at me, and what starts off as a whisper manifests itself to something bigger and this thing, this being, he is on my back, in my mind and on both shoulders and begins to scream at me. This devil on my shoulder tells me I'm worthless and of no use. And as sad it sounds, the only way I can release him is by harming myself more with little regard for the consequences of my actions. When I cut, I am calm.

"It's not every day. Some days the urges are easier to resist than others, but they are always there, and thoughts of self-harm return, especially when I have been drinking, which of late is most days. The embarrassment of a scar will never beat the enthralment of a cut; when I cut, I feel alive. I understand how sad, how grotesque and narcissistic that sounds, but it is what it is. I shouldn't be telling you all of this. I'm sorry."

He hugs me. I stare at the floor and cower up in shame as the last of my undiluted words leave my lips.

"You have nothing to be sorry for. Ask for help and see someone, a professional who will help – you shouldn't feel like a failure. You should talk to someone. It might not be as scary as you think it will be; I don't mind coming with you. We are both hurting, a little broken and lost, but let's help each other. Just try to stay positive and make your friend proud of you; she wouldn't want to see you hurting like this. I'm here for you. If you need someone to talk to, call, just call me."

We finish our drinks and both look out as faint, flickered flashes of sunshine touch the water's edge. Ollie looks at me. I feel myself struggling. I start to panic. I shouldn't have told him so much. I pant loudly and feel my consciousness start to fall; I crash my head hard into his shoulder and I curse God and I sob. Tears touch my dry, broken lips. I take big, deep breaths. I breath in then out, in out, in out, in out. He holds me tight and goosebumps dance on my arms and the hairs on the back of my neck stand to attention like guards on Her Majesty's service.

When he is next to me, the negative noises in my head cease. I wish we could stay forever in this single moment. I close my eyes; when he holds me every bit of darkness, hurt and pain stops. Tears fill my eyes. I am lost in my black hole. He holds me tight and I weep like a baby in his arms. The panic and fear both stop, and I feel very stoned. I am stationary and stuck to the bench but feel OK. The daggers remain but the contractions are not quite so harsh.

My head swirls and everything spins. I am being transported to a far, dark and distant place; still I spin, but his touches calm me and the sirens in my head slow. I clamp myself around his side. He holds me and it feels good. He has drilled through my slab of bleakness; he has infiltrated my block of darkness and the weight around me comes crashing down.

"I don't deserve a friend like you. I'm sorry, you are going through enough yourself."

He stands and gives me a hug and a kiss on the cheek, then turns his back and walks away. I watch in desperation as he departs. The distance between us grows until his perfect frame disappears to a small dot before fading entirely. All I can do is stand and watch until he is no more. He fades. I feel numb. He departs and the feeling of slow motion stops. My insides are red and angry as beaming red collides with bruised purple as an explosion of anger showers my mind.

I feel nerves, frightened at being alone and what I will end up doing to myself. I am scared; emptiness washes over me. The pit of my stomach lurches. He is gone. I feel sick. He is gone. I feel faint. He is gone.

April 20th

Hot sun streams through my windows. I wake up sweating, but instead of reaching for the glass of water I instead opt for the half-empty bottle of red wine beside it. I drink in huge gulps and slam the empty bottle back on my bedside table, causing the water in the glass to shimmer. The bliss of booze has disappeared. I have noticed a shift in balance. The euphoria and excitement alcohol once offered has reduced. I feel myself struggling and start to panic. With a powerful urge to drink I go the freezer. I pour the remains of a vodka bottle into a glass, add some ice and drink it neat in a single gulp to quieten my emotions.

My self-harm escalates at breakneck speed. It has become my obsession. It consumes me. I have entered a world where it's all I think of. I worry my cutting has escalated to the point it warrants medical intervention. As each day passes, my wounds are deeper and cuts more frequent. They migrate to other areas of my body. I look down at my arms, my stomach and the bloody mess that I have caused. Splashes of red paint my thin, shaking thighs and broken scabs weep on my mucky, mutilated wrists. I have stopped asking myself why I do this and my motivation behind it.

Whilst at times I feel disgust, shame, pity and fear, there are also rare moments of incredible relief, intrigue and excitement, or perhaps this is just me in denial, doing my utmost to paint a positive light for the various memos etched on my skin. The scars I wear serve as a reminder of who I am. As I harm, I get a hit. I think how sad it is; this, my first taste of hedonism.

I've tried to stop. I've tried dancing prickly drawing pins along my thigh and pushing sharp, spikey ice cubes into my ribs. I have tried it all, but nothing comes close. My disappointment is like that of an alcoholic expecting the same buzz from a shot of alcohol-free absinthe. In rare moments of clarity, I wonder if my physical evidence of self-harm is enough to convince myself something is wrong, but these feelings pass as quickly as they enter my troubled mind.

There are times when I am tempted to cry for help but worry what people will think and where I will end up. I don't want to be assessed, labelled and pigeonholed. I think about mental health nurses, counsellors and psychotherapists, and what I could gain from them, but my self-hate overrides this. I don't want to take up the time of decent, honest people; their time is far better served on someone with a desire to be saved.

I don't want a doctor stitching me up, making me feel as if I have committed a sin, placing a sympathetic, reassuring hand on my wounded shoulder. No one has the right to heal my screaming wounds and make my pain bearable. This is my pain, and my skin. I refuse to place myself in front of supportive professionals who assume they might just know the answer to the torment that circulates around me because they completed a master's degree in psychology or, even worse, feel they "know my battle" because they too struggled with self-harm and self-hate.

I don't want to sit in a bright room with my dark mind and answer awkward questions which someone feels they already know the answers to and be told how vulnerable I am, but in time, with baby steps, I will improve. I don't want therapy. I don't want to understand my self-harm or the science behind it. I don't want to get better, as getting better means I am conscious and alert to Daisy and her passing. That feeling of my loss, my pain, scares me a great deal more than my self-harm and suicide.

With therapy will come prescribed medications; this temporary measure will no doubt turn into addiction. I will end up so numb and spaced out I might as well be dead anyway. No medication is going to bring back my best friend. I am not naïve enough to believe medication will make my problem disappear. Therapy will involve someone trying to open a locked box of memories that brought me to here and discuss the loss of my parents, but it's quite simple. I lost Daisy and feel as though I have no right to live.

The stress of therapy would no doubt cause an even greater episode of self-harm. The road to recovery is long and not one I wish to contemplate. Should I take that path I lose all control. I will not allow myself to lose control. The thought of giving up this relief feels me with dread. I am not able to imagine a time I will stop with my self-harm. I simply will not allow someone to take this pleasure from me. I think about this for several minutes and it fills me with rage. I feel the pressure building inside me. It inflates and the pressure continues. My pain increases and the hurt in my head grows larger still. It looms.

I close my eyes and I am transported back to a year earlier. I am in a tulip field with Daisy in Amsterdam. We are lying down next to each other in fits of laughter as the magic mushrooms we took earlier work their way through our skinny, giggling bodies. Our knees collide as we roll around fields in fits of laughter. Above us clouds turn into cartoon characters as distorted, surreal visual colours beam down, washing over us.

Thoughts of Daisy and me consume my tenuous mind, and the pressure in my head mounts. I think about the time we were late for a double date. We are desperately chasing the number seventy-three bus and Daisy's heel breaks; she falls in a puddle, causing me to laugh so hard I wet myself. I think about the good times and then my mind reverts to the end. I am crouched next to her, holding her shaking, tiny hand as she whimpers and wails, telling me she is sorry that she will never get to be my bridesmaid.

My pain grows. I need it to stop, as my head is unable to deal with the hurt and the angst. I feel unhinged, tense and agitated. I am now on my back as excruciating noises reverberate in my head. The pressure builds; it holds nothing back and knows how weak I am. It comes in waves, harder, faster, harder and faster. My mood becomes more violent as sharp daggers swing back and forth through my foggy mind. I am waiting to implode; I am exhausted, angry and my mind is warped.

My only option is to reach for the blade. I pierce my pain to deflate the relentless storm of anger and terror. I carve increasingly deep and angry wounds into my skin. My world goes into slow motion. My self-harm allows my rage to calm. My racing mind slowly becoming more lethargic. I cry from the relief; I cry from the pain. I am released. I cry. The only light at the end of my tunnel, my self-harm.

I lack the motivation, dedication and commitment to save myself, but that's OK. I don't want to overcome my self-harm. All I crave is an avenue to inner peace from the constant torment.

May

Ollie

Paradise Rise is an intimidating, fortress-like, dated block of flats and not the pretty view I had envisaged. Bleak, grey, drab concrete looms large, with front lawns in urgent need of tender loving care. Rolls of rotting carpets and sofas are piled knee-high in front of brutalist architecture. I walk towards Ada's flat, my head a barrel of excitement and my body a bag of niggling nerves. My hands shake and my heart leaps and hurdles.

I call Ada to let her know I have arrived and take the lift to the ninth floor as instructed. As I escalate, I look out to the Thames, watching in wonder as it bends, twists and churns. When I arrive, the door is already slightly ajar. I step inside and walk into her front room. The ceilings are high and the walls tastefully decorated in a magnolia white, with a feature wall a burnt shade of saffron.

There is a coffee table in the middle of the room, with an armchair either side, both covered in a multi-coloured paisley pattern. There are flowers in a vase. The petals, violet, white and canary yellow. Above the table is a Lowry print, housed within a warping, gold, chipped frame which is coming apart at one end. On the table is a laptop with a webpage open: "Help with Self-Harm". Ada enters the room and quickly but quietly pushes her laptop shut, unsure if I have seen. She is wearing tight charcoal jeans and a claret-coloured cardigan.

"You look nice," I say.

"Thanks, so do you," she says, blushing as she nervously looks to the floor, avoiding eye contact.

We share a cigarette then flag down a taxi and travel the short distance to Kings Cross, where we arrive at the gastro bar and sit down at our pre-booked table. I look at her and can't stop staring. Despite all around us possessing weather-lashed looks, Ada looks perfect. She sticks out like a sore thumb.

She goes to the bar to order our food. In the corner of my eye I see a guy talking to Ada. He is in her face and speaking loudly. She looks uncomfortable in his company. He is with two friends; they stand either side of Ada, laughing as their friend spits loud words in Ada's direction.

He is sweaty-faced and leery, with tensed muscles, his hair greasy and thick. The trio look like they have been drinking all day and are up to no good.

Ada turns from him and walks away as he pulls at her cardigan, desperately trying to pull her back, she struggles and successfully pulls herself free from his filthy, festering hands. She returns to our table with our drinks as the trio whisper and stare and continue to look in our direction with a fixed glaze.

They laugh then each chuck another generous shot into their mouths and slam the small shot glasses back down on the bar in unison with such might it startles me. A short while later, Ada walks to the bathroom and the same guy stands in her way. He is talking to her; I am unable to make out what he says. She looks uncomfortable and nervous. He pulls her closer to him, their bodies collide and his friends laugh.

Ada looks uneasy and scared. She looks at the floor and tries to pull herself past him, but this time his grip is too strong. He holds her waist. Ada struggles and turns to look at me. I leave my seat at speed and run over to him with repercussions and any possible error of judgement far away from my anxious, angry mind.

I am now in front of him. Ada screams. I look into his glazed eyes and see nothing but evil. The guy is big. The muscles in his arm and twitch and flicker.

"Can you leave me friend alone, please?" I plead.

"What are you going to do about it, mate?" he says.

Everything about him is cold, dark and twisted. His eyes, his facial expression, his mannerisms and temper. His pale, angry complexion frightens me. He now has Ada's hair wrapped around one hand; again he asks me, "I said, what the fuck are you going to do about it, mate?"

He looks at me with a fixed stare. He has the devil in his bloodshot eyes and he lunges at me. He hates me and he hits me. For a person of his weight and size the pace at which he moves and strikes takes me by surprise. My body goes tense and Ada shakes free and is now screaming. My eyes dart desperately, longing for help; there is no one. A young couple in the distance make eye contact with me to see what is going on and then quickly revert their heads back down to their evening meal. There is no security. Ada and I are now separated as tears run the length of her face.

He thumps me in the ribs, twice in quick succession, then in the face. He hits me harder than I've been hit in my life. The force at which he connects with my nose causes it to explode. I hear and feel it break; it pops, causing an explosion of cartilage, blood and bile, and makes me gag as I throw up a sticky mess all over myself. I am all at sea; my knees buckle. I try to re-group, but he is too quick.

My lip splits; the blood runs quickly into my waiting mouth and warms my tongue. My world goes dark, my legs limpen and I collapse, hitting the stone-cold floor. I feel scared. I want it all to stop. I want to run. The room feels as if it is shrinking in size and the walls cave in. My insides shake like a washing machine. I struggle to breathe. I take big gasps of air and try to stay calm. My body spasms in unimaginable pain. I try to kick out, but my legs are too tired.

"Stop, please, stop, oh my God, please," I scream, but my words are muffled with tears and my desperate, panting plea ignored.

I lie tight in a ball, protecting my head with my hand, and scream once more for him to stop. His friends pick me up and I am struck again – this time half a dozen punches to the stomach and another to the face. I throw up and taste the foul combination of sick and blood. Fists of fury penetrate my fallen frame. He continues with a volley of blows back and forth until his large hands grow tired of connecting with my dripping, sticky face.

He strikes again, this time a brutal blow to the back of my head. He is relentless, ferocious, vicious and violent. I feel his heavy weight on top of me and his rough hands hold my throat. He towers above me and is now on top of me. His hands are tight around my throat and I struggle for air.

I open my eyes and he is still in front of me. His hard glare paralyses me. Everything stops making sense. Angry, muffled words are shouted. Shouted sentences get jumbled up. My panic is sharp and my body limp. My face is numb. I feel like I am drowning. My pain is everywhere. I feel wet blood all over me. My top is drenched as damp beads run the length of my chest. I am unsure if it is sweat or blood. My chest is a bloody mess as his hands continue to strike and shake violently in my direction with rage.

My head is all over the place and my whole existence in the balance. My human spirit deteriorates; I abandon all faith in it. The battle inside me begins to falter. I see myself failing. My limbs hang loosely beneath me. I keep my eyes shut and pass momentarily to somewhere else and pretend this is not happening.

I don't want this. People stare. I feel shame and hurt. I hear screaming. A voice behind me screams, "*Knife, knife, he's got a knife.*" There are lots of people now, faces I fail to recognise, but they appear like they are on my side. Everything goes into slow motion. I feel blood trickle down my nose. He looks at me; still the devil dances in his eyes and sweat pours from his head as he swiftly moves from side to side and comes at me again.

Before he can reach me, Ada jumps on his back. She pulls herself up and latches her right hand on his stubbly face, digging her nails in deep, pulling her whole weight down to the cold ground and bringing his wounded face with her. Nail wounds run from his right eye to just above the left of his twitching, swollen lip. She punches the knife from his grasp and clenches her crooked teeth into his fleshy arm. I hear metal hit the ground but am unable to see it. He breaks free and has his hand round my throat again.

I am motionless, clueless and defenceless. I am helpless and gag. I feel myself black out as my struggle for consciousness intensifies. But then he lets go and it stops. He looks deep into my eyes, but our stare is stretched as in my blurred vision I see two men grabbing him and he is moved away from me and pulled back. Tight arms snake around me. My body moves so quickly my feet don't touch the floor.

Ada and I are now outside; the cold air hits my wounds. There is blood all over my hands. I am unsure if it is his or mine. I pay no mind. All noise has stopped. It is now silence. We are pushed inside a taxi; it is warm, and we start to move. I turn around to look out of the window. Those who attacked me chase our speeding vehicle. Their mouths are open; they make angry gesture with their fists. I do not hear their words. Our machine is quicker than their legs. The people grow smaller; the screaming dims. All around me is silence. My breathing slows.

We tangle ourselves together and touch. I feel comfort, warmth and safety surround me. Her cardigan is covered in rips. She has gaping holes all over her jeans; her face is weary and torn. She holds my freezing, shaking hands; she holds me like she never wants to let go. She looks as bad as I feel. I feel guilt. I touch my face; it rings.

I lay my throbbing, heavy head on her lap and let out a huge sigh of relief. From the taxi window I struggle to see just a slim line of the murky, dark sky. The back of my neck is cold. My body trembles. I close my eyes and see stars and spiral into an emptiness of intense proportions.

After what seems an eternity we safely arrive back at Paradise Rise. I limp and struggle as I pull myself from the taxi to the lift. From the lift I stagger to her front door then into her bathroom. I lock the door then lie on the floor. Every part of me vibrates. The room shakes and spins. I attempt to stand up and this makes it worse. I feel giddy and sick. I fall back down. I am sick all over the floor and all over my trousers and I cry. I feel a rush and wave of anger.

She bangs on the door and I pull myself up. I check my pockets; they are empty. I look at my gruesome reflection. Black, blue, bruised and bloodied. Pale, thin and drained. I am tired beyond belief. My top is drenched from blood and sweat. My chest heaves and my head is a wreck. I cry from pain. I cry from relief, relief that I am still here. I squat and pour handfuls of cold water against my damaged face. I drink the water; my perished throat eases as my thirst is quenched. My hands tremble; they are clean but shake furiously.

May 8th

I awake in unfamiliar surroundings on a sofa bed too small for my aching, wounded frame. It takes several seconds for me to remind myself I am at Ada's flat. My top is tainted a deep, dirty red, my breathing spits and spurts, and my stomach's tight. I delicately finger my swollen mouth. The pain still rings. I stare at my fingers. They are like sausages, bruised and sore, too large and disproportionate from the skinny hands they hang from.

"Hi," she simply says as she nibbles at her bottom lip in a mischievous manner.

I look at Ada and take my time with each stare. I stare at her. Her lips, her face, I stare. She catches me looking at her and I quickly avert my eyes to the floor. I take in all her beauty, absorbing and observing her as if each glance is my last.

"You look so frightened when I catch you looking at me. You shouldn't; I like it."

Ada walks to the kitchen to make us both a coffee. I stare at her again as butterflies gather and glide within me.

She sits cross-legged in front of me, wearing a navy T-shirt a few sizes too large for her skinny frame. With warm cotton wool she attentively wipes and removes the dry blood from my brow and tells me to keep still. I close my eyes and imagine kissing her and momentarily I'm floating away with Ada, our feet no longer on the ground. She scratches her head with sharp, red painted nails. I gaze at her nails and I lose all concentration. She has plasters on her wrists and scratches on her left forearm.

We gaze at each other and sit in silence as she finishes fixing me up. She pulls my eyes shut with her soft, small fingers and kisses me. It takes me by surprise. I open my mouth and feel her tongue. She tastes as beautiful as I expected her to. We hold hands, we sit and we kiss. We kiss for what seems like an eternity. I think of Grace and am showered in guilt but am unable to control myself.

My insides tingle. Our tongues collide and touch and dance once more; we are united in pain, united in rapture.

As I hold her, I am aware how different her body feels to Grace's. She is close to me. I feel a warm glow.

I lift the heavy fringe from her face and kiss her again. I feel like the whole world has stopped and every bit of darkness, hurt and pain is swept away. We collide, we kiss and fall to the floor like crumpled pieces of paper, our bodies entwined. I feel her erect nipples on my chest and goosebumps on tiny, damaged forearms. I hold her hand and tell her that when I'm with her the world is a wonderful, beautiful place. I wish that time could stop so we could forever stay in this moment of sheer bliss.

She puts her arm around me and asks if she can kiss me again. She tells me she has never been kissed by someone who cares about her. She talks of her broken heart and tells me that each time in her past when she has met someone new her hopeful heart has ended up broken. She asks me why I like her and tells me she doesn't deserve me. We lose the afternoon immersed in one another as our bodies entwine while we touch, talk and lay bare our hopes, dreams and fears.

May 19th

The morning is noisy. The day sings to me. My ears feel more open and more alert. I look at the vibrant, technicolour streets. Shafts of sunshine yellow the leaves of the trees outside my view. I look at the trees. My phone rings once; it rings twice. It doesn't stop ringing. I ignore it. It rings again. On the fifth time I pick it up. It's Vinnie.

"Thank goodness you answered. The sun is shining and it's your lucky day. I'm five minutes from Holloway.

I won't take no for an answer either. Get yourself ready; I will see you shortly." He abruptly hangs up his phone as I desperately search for some clean clothes.

I hear the engine before I see the car. It roars with the ferocity of a lion. I peer outside and see Vinnie. He sees me and waves from his Porsche 911. I quickly make my way outside. He gives me a hug and looks at my clothes with a glint of sorrow etched upon his chiselled face. We drive to Notting Hill, where we park and then spend the next few hours roaming around Portobello Road. We stop in a hipster coffee shop and wash down posh pasties with expensive coffee beans poured delicately into glass cups finished with whipped cream and a dusting of cinnamon sugar.

We walk into a tailors; it's a highly civilised establishment with beautiful high ceilings and exquisite furnishings. Vinnie hugs various members of staff like they are long-lost friends. They laugh, they joke and pat each other's backs. He introduces me to them all. I sit down on a large teal-coloured Chesterfield armchair and play with my phone, feeling slightly out of place.

"Ollie, come here." Vinnie hands me a jacket. I try it on; it fits me like a glove. The price tag is beyond staggering and I place the garment back on the hanger.

We leave the shop and I briefly walk ahead. I turn around and Vinnie is no longer with me. Through the window I see he is still in the shop. He stands at the counter writing out a cheque whilst the eager assistant neatly folds the jacket I tried on into a thick black bag. He catches me looking through the window and smiles. He hands me the suit bag. I go to thank him. He interrupts me, saying, "Don't mention it – you will need it where we are heading," as he hands me the bag.

We are back in his car and we drive; eventually we arrive at the Dorchester hotel. We are assisted out by two large, friendly men. We pass immaculate cars and walk through a large glass revolving door. I look around at the most luxurious of surroundings. The air tastes expensive as scented perfume glides through my nostrils and I feel a warm glow of contentment. The restaurant is busy; there is French jazz music playing. The room is intriguing, with lavish interiors and furniture.

The bag feels heavy. I go to the bathroom and look inside the bag. In the mirror I survey my face and what remains of the damage. It has been a few weeks, but my face still carries the carnage of my encounter. There is an expensive shirt and trousers to match the jacket. Beneath these are a pair of smart black shoes. I return from the toilet and Vinnie smiles at me.

I sit down and a handsome waiter excitedly greets Vinnie. "Vinnie, how wonderful to see you." He kisses Vinnie on the cheek.

"Reni, this is Oliver, a good friend of mine."

Reni shakes my hand and tells me he will take good care of us. I have a wonderfully tender ruby-red ribeye steak. We then share a cheeseboard almost the length of the table with chutneys and crackers.

"I brought you here because I wanted to talk to you. I understand what you are doing, you and Ada, but just be careful. Take your time. There's no rush. Jumping in with both feet and diving straight in at the deep end might seem like fun right now, but you could both end up drowning. Tell me to mind my own business, but just tread careful. What drove you together, could just as quickly drive you apart.

"You have both been through so much in such a short space of time. I see the grief and pain you both wear; it's still so raw and new. Throwing yourself into a relationship can seem like the obvious quick solution, but just be careful, mate. I've been there, done that, got the T-shirt. The chances of you hurting her or vice versa are much stronger owing to the situation you are both in. After I lost Sophie, I did lots of things I'm not proud of to make myself feel better. The short-term fix can often make the long-term road to recovery even tougher. You both deserve to be happy, but I don't want to see either of you getting hurt after what you have already both been through. I'm just trying to protect your feelings.

"I see you improve each week and marvel at your strength, your determination to not let grief get the better of you. With Ada, I must be honest, I worry. Companionship, love, the things you shared with Grace – I get why you are chasing them with Ada. Any human heart wants that, and chasing those feelings makes sense and might appear to be the rational solution. But you have time. There is no rush, no race; she isn't going anywhere. She likes you; I can see it in her eyes. Just take it easy – good things come to those who wait, right?" Vinnie looks at me, stands up and moves to my side of the table. He crouches down and gives me a tight hug.

I digest his words and thank him for his concern. I go to the bathroom; when I return Vinnie is paying the bill. He drops me back home and I feel embarrassed as we pull up to my flat. I thank him for everything, watch as he drives off and think about our relationship – so odd. Incompatible strangers tossed together like ingredients that shouldn't complement each other but do.

I wake alone in Ada's small and compact front room. Cautiously tiptoeing, conscious my heavy footsteps could startle and wake her, I open the window of her ninth-floor flat in hope of removing the musty morning smell. Several minutes later Ada enters the room; her silhouette slides in front of mine.

She walks towards me and passes; I smell her. Her hair brushes my arm. I am taken aback by her beauty. She is picture-perfect. The sun on my Sunday morning. Her face shines like a beacon; her rosy, freckled cheeks and gracefulness looks out of place against the dull, grey, drab morning and bleak landscape that lurks behind her.

She makes me a cup of instant coffee and we share a blueberry muffin that tastes like it's close to its expiry date. She seems more distant than last night; our conversation that flowed now feels more stationary. I ask her what's wrong and almost feel like I am in the way and my company is unwanted.

"I'm fine, just tired." She sighs as she shrugs off my concerns.

As we leave her flat a gaggle of youths combine and stare at us. One of the group shouts something. I play dumb and choose to ignore this, pretending I can't hear. I find it peculiar Ada would choose to reside somewhere so intimidating. The claustrophobic concrete looks at me like it knows I am not from round here. Loud music beats and cats scream as a collage of desperation and gloom surrounds me. She tells me she is used to it. I don't want her to be used to anywhere that could harm her. I wish I could bubble-wrap her bones.

Wind cracks against the skin of my bruised face as we wander down a dark alley. I touch her hand and Ada nervously places her small hand in mine, unsure she is doing the right thing; I sense her hesitation. I catch our shadows on the pavement and marvel at how suited they are. I hold her hand tightly and it feels almost like part of my body. My insides glow. A feeling of warmth and contentment washes over me – a welcome feeling I was unsure I would experience after Grace.

We walk to Ada and Daisy's bench. We sit down; as we do, I feel her touch and am instantly at ease. When she speaks, I listen, not allowing myself to miss a single word. I lean in for a kiss. As our faces touch we breathe into each other's nostrils. She leaves my mouth with a taste of blueberry. We kiss. She closes her eyes. I keep my eyes wide open. I feel an immediate and powerful surge.

Regardless of how tired her clothes might look she has a natural air of sophistication and class. I feel a dull moron in comparison. As we are sit, I notice a small hole in my trousers by my groin. I put my left leg in front of my right to cover it, hoping she won't notice. She does; Ada laughs. I feel awkward, ridiculous and extremely unglamorous. The hours pass; they pass too quickly. I wish for the clocks to stop. We talk. I talk too quickly at times and mess my words up on several occasions. I try my best to be funny, kind and caring. All the things I thought perhaps I was not capable of after Grace's passing.

We are now back at her flat and on her sofa. Inside I tremble. Goosebumps gather all over me. She is on top of me, straddling, me with a leg either side of my waist. Cheap hairspray fills my mouth as her perfume consumes the air. She kisses my cheek and I feel her lips mould around my cheek. She is on top of me and our tongues touch. She pants and crumples on tops of me.

I feel euphoria, a feeling of indescribable, extreme ecstasy I have missed so very much. I feel bliss as all negativity drifts away and disappears. It's sucked and swallowed away from me and my head clears as my all hurt and all my pain is transported to somewhere else. I feel stronger and brighter. My thoughts are clearer as I see clear light before me. I am transformed to a happy place, so high and mighty that only the elite are allowed entry. I hold her and my feelings intensify.

I look at her and I want her. I imagine lifting her into her bed, undressing her and touching every piece of her. I imagine me on top of her, her back arched and giving her everything she wants, our bodies entwining and shaking as we climax simultaneously. I feel shaky and want to kiss her but feel she is holding something back. I find myself both starting and finishing conversations and am conscious I am putting in more work into this than she.

She hugs me then bursts into tears. She pulls away. A tear falls down her face. She looks scared and nervous; she is holding back. I feel that there is a side, a troubled side, a wall and guard that is up. A wall that's not going to be easy to break down. I want to hold her, break through, smash the wall and tell Ada of her self-worth and make her see just what this is and what she means to me.

We are both now in just our underwear; I look at her arms, she looks at me and she stops. Her mood, her mind, her words switch, and she leaps up from my lap. She looks worried. She is holding back. I try to put my arm around her. She pulls away and leans her head towards the floor as if the carpet is more exciting than my face. She sits next to me, keeping distant. She lifts her hand towards mine.

"I'm sorry, I can't do this. I'd prefer it if you didn't touch me. I'm sorry," she says as she quickly retreats, pulls away and puts her cardigan back on at speed. "I think it's best you leave. I don't think I can do this anymore. I tried, but I can't. I really wanted this to work, but maybe it's the right thing but at the wrong time. I don't know, I need some space. I just feel like I need to breathe. This is all getting too claustrophobic. I'm sorry."

Her mood changes as her hands shake wildly and violently in my direction. Her voice grows to a higher, spikier tone, and her expression becomes more animated

"Sorry, what do you mean? What have I said? I'm sorry, I thought this was what you wanted too? If this is about me and Grace, I feel ready – I thought you did?" I plea as my words cut across hers in desperation and panic.

She continues, "Maybe we are just getting a little ahead of ourselves. Has it ever crossed your mind the only reason we are spending so much time together is because we are both so sad, lost and lonely, and we have nothing else to focus our attention on?

"I don't want to be your last resort because there is nothing else out there. I get it, you are lonely and bored, and

I'm the first thing to came along. A quick solution that helps mask your pain. What if this isn't real? What if what we are doing doesn't work out? Has that crossed your mind?

"This is desperation, lust and not love? I'm not anything special, I know that, and you do too. Look at us, Ollie. I am just as broken as you. I need to focus on myself before I can even begin to think about anyone else. I need to repair and work on me before you. That must be my focus. This thing isn't. It's secondary. It's not fair on me or you. Ollie, you are a nice person, but there are much safer options than me.

"Soon enough it will go wrong, as these things always tend to do. It will fizzle and burn and morph into friendship. We will then become friends who become strangers. We will then stop all contact and we will be left lost and broken and worse off than we were before our paths crossed. Tell me I'm wrong, go on, Ollie, tell me I am wrong."

"Ada, please, I thought things were OK. If you feel things are moving too fast, let's just take a sideways step and slow things down, it's fine. Please relax. I didn't go to Julie's with the intention of this, treating it like some cattle market then just developing feelings for the first person I saw. I like you because of who you are, Ada, not because I'm desperate.

"When I'm with you everything feels better. I feel like a stronger, much-improved version of me. You bring out the version of me I wish to be, the version of me I thought I had lost. If you want me to leave I will, but please don't think my feelings are fake; that's not fair."

She looks at her bandaged arms then back at me. "The reason we are here and in each other's company is that we both lost something. You can't just lose something then find something and expect for the new to replace the old. This isn't like losing a pair of shoes and buying a new pair. This is emotions, feelings. My mental anguish is mine. I hate myself every single minute of every passing day. I feel non-existent. I don't love myself, so how can I be expected to develop feelings for someone else? Please, I'm begging you, just give me, give us some space."

She shuts the door and I leave her flat, tears riotously run down my face, and I hear a glass smash on the other side of the front door I have just closed, as Vinnie's words of wisdom echo through the contents of my mind.

June

Ada

June 14th

I awake surprised, having made it through another night, disappointed at my failure to choke on my own vomit. The voices in my head rise early and the demons come hissing, it is not yet 7am. Dark thoughts and high-pitched voices goad me. The voices scream, preventing me from a peaceful existence. They tell me I am a shameful, revolting human with no worth on this earth. I have reached breaking point. I am angry, scared and alone, conscious that my future hangs by a thread.

I struggle to stand, barely able to lift the weight of my head and walk to the bathroom. I look in the mirror, my enemy, and despise what I see, unable to tolerate my own reflection. Big, black, wicked circles bulge beneath my eyes, stealing all light, as evil thoughts continue to dance. I stare at my earrings and think how ridiculous they look, another

79

failed attempt at improving my ghastly appearance. I look at the skin they hang from and, in a fit of fury, lash out at myself, grasping the ring from my left ear and pulling it out in one clean foul swoop.

My outburst of frustration tears my skin and a thin shower of deep red drops to my bony cold shoulder. When this started, I was safe cutting with no intention of causing serious damage to myself. This has now changed, with my mind hell-bent on causing maximum carnage. I try to think of any positives in my life but not a single one comes to mind. My feeling of emptiness leads me to drink; after drinking I take cocaine. I then drink faster, quicker and harder to level out the cocaine that helps to quieten the rampant whistles and noises gurgling in my absent mind.

I have withdrawn myself from all social activity, preferring my own company. A self-imposed quarantine of sorts. Self-isolation. I seldom speak to friends and no longer attend Julie's support class. The last person I saw was Ollie, a few weeks ago. I will only leave the house to feed my addictions. My daily chat with Daisy from our bench has got less frequent. It's been three weeks since I last went to work, informing them I needed some time out. Since Daisy departed my mind was somewhere else. The lights were on but no one home; perhaps I should never have gone back at all.

As predicted my relationship with Ollie has waned and is no more. All good things must come to an end and all that. It was inevitable. Why someone like Ollie would choose to invest his time and energy in me is beyond my mind to comprehend. I know his feelings for me are false anyway and I grew suspicious of his intentions. He only wanted me for a quick thrill, a cheap leg over; he has nothing else, so opted for me. I'm not naive enough to believe he would like me. It was desperation that led him to my door. He lost his wife and needed something to fill his time and I was that. He was too much, anyway, and I began to feel suffocated.

I have thought about getting help, but those thoughts leave my mind as quickly as they enter; besides, I don't want anyone getting too close to me, advising me how to live my life and looking at me in sorrow and pity and trying to help. I barely have the will to live and the help and support that could save me I shall never receive because ultimately the truth is, I don't deserve it. Negative thoughts manifest my tormented mind as my paranoia intensifies. I look out my window and am sure the faces looking back are talking about me. Lippy kids on bikes cup their hands and scream obscenities in my direction. I hear whispers, ranting and screaming then hide behind the curtain. I hear emergency sirens, convinced that they are coming for me.

I turn on the TV to try to rest my mind but am only able to concentrate on the content for a short burst of time before my mind starts to wander. Impatiently I flick from channel to channel until I stop. There is a pretty girl holding hands with a tall, dark, handsome, bronzed man. They are young, she is pregnant and her skin glows. She has big, plump, red lips and her shoes look expensive. He is wearing a crisp white shirt that flutters in the late afternoon wind, revealing a muscular stomach and a large gold watch. They walk in the garden and smile at one another, both content and happy they have found their place in the sun.

I pour a large glass of vodka and down it in one and watch the couple for a few minutes longer. With no pre-warning my mind switches. It sets it off and spills into the more evocative enthralling prospect of a tear, burn or splitting of my skin. The words on the television mumble and become mute. I can still see the couple but am no longer able to hear their words. The compulsion of indulging in my self-harm is too powerful and intense to fight. It's something sinful, savage and forbidden, and the force is too strong; it won't let up. I am now sat on my hands, hoping and praying the need to harm passes.

I try to ignore it, but the noises in my head increase; they throb and terrify me. I look at the blade in the kitchen and brace myself, scared of the inevitable. I feel my thighs shake in perverted anticipation as my distress levitates to uncontrollable, unmanageable heights. I look down at a weeping wound on my left thigh from a previous assault. My right unscathed thigh then begins twitching intensely, yearning for his turn and his release.

The noise transforms to such a level that I have no choice and I scream. I scream so loud I want the world to hear my trauma and rage. I seize the moment and clutch the blade and, with clenched fist, plunge and propel the knife deep in my thigh in a violent rage against myself. My legs give way and I fall to the floor; I cry but feel relief. The nagging and shouting has stopped. A gentle warmth rushes through me, swallowing me whole. With self-harm I have learnt a new way of being and at my own pace am now able to get through my day.

The fidgeting has stopped. The pain throbs and my fresh wound runs but the voices in my head are now mute as my mind's transferred to a calmer state. The couple on TV are now in the kitchen. The charming man excitedly rubs his partner's bulging belly and informs the glamorous presenter they would like to make an offer several thousand pounds below the asking price.

June 26th

I wake in a cold sweat and feel horrendous. My world is starved of all colour as bleak shadows loom. The voices in my head rise early once more. They beat and bang and clatter and clunk. The sound of sorrow sings. It raises its ugly head and won't let up. My skin crawls with rage. I long for a silence, for peace, for a clear mind. I must dull the noise. I wish to fade away. I'm not strong. I am a coward. I am weak. I have reached my end. I wipe my tears. I've lost all strength, courage and pride. My body is thin. My muscles sag. Enough is enough. Today will be my end. My mind is made up. I can't fight this any longer. I don't want the constant confrontation.

I am a coward and have let this win. As death draws ever closer, I begin to let go and feel almost acceptance to the inevitable. My mind slows. I sob so hard I can barely breathe. My tears collect. I feel stretched to the limits of both emptiness and sorrow. I feel myself decaying in the most unpleasant way. My body feels too heavy to hold but too light to support me. All of me hurts. My loneliness is so vast it covers me in blackness and stops me from thinking. Like a noose around my neck it grapples me and tightens its hold. I don't want to be alone.

Wearing only my dressing gown and a pair of slippers, I pick up my handbag and leave my front door at speed. Deep red and glorious orange daggers sail across the blue morning sky, causing me to squint. The lift is out of service, so I walk down the dingy stairwell, narrowly avoiding young children making the most of the uncollected rubbish bags for an early-morning game of hide-and-seek. I walk down a narrower corridor and pass destitute families struggling in squalor in a vast concrete slum. Refuse piles up and sewage drips from poorly maintained pipes; the smell of damp lingers.

On the ground floor I pass cracked walls and crumpled, desperate faces of drug addicts thirsty for their next fix, politely queuing in single file outside a boarded-up flat. I keep my face fixed to the floor to avoid any unwelcome stares and crouch beneath local council scaffolding, dancing over discarded needles and limp narrow streets to our bench by the water's edge.

I hear a noise behind me; it shrieks. The screaming intensifies. My mind is riddled with dark thoughts. The wailing is now not less than a metre behind me. I feel its breath dance across the nape of my neck. I can't let them catch me, so I run. I run faster than my wounded legs can carry me. I trip and fall; my knee lands on broken glass, causing it to tear my skin. I look behind me, panting wildly; there is no one there, the noise just in my head. My knee is caked in blood and my hands are filthy. I have lost all hope and all dignity.

I sit down at our bench and carefully remove the small, sharp fragments of glass from my thin, shaking knee. In doing so I touch a bone; it makes me wince and feel queasy. I remove the bandage from my wrist and use this to mop the blood from my knee, tightly tying it around my wound. I look across the water. A sprawling housing estate consumes my view. Abandoned, empty, crumbling apartments, haunted by crime, with most of the windows now replaced with bricks.

I look out to my friend and talk to her.

"Daisy, I don't think I'm very well. I don't know which way to turn or where to start. I'm frightened and scared." My knee throbs and the blood is dark and thick. I feel it tickle as warm liquid runs the length of my naked leg over my trembling calf and down to the sole of my foot.

"I'm not strong enough to carry this heartbreak. Every living day is an excruciating, painful, recurring dream. Even when I'm numb it's agonising. I am stuck on a rollercoaster, an endless loop of anguish, consumed with this suffering. I just can't shake it and the weight of it crushes me. I'm going to be seeing you soon; please don't be mad when you see me. I'm sorry I let you down. I'm sorry."

I sob and I scream. I want someone to find me and hear my yelp. Someone, anyone to save me. I look around; there is no one. Waves of grief crash over me, buckling my knees and taking my breath away. I am falling apart and wail like a newborn baby. My cries get louder and I look around; still there is no one. It is just me and the stillness of the water's edge.

I return home and the tears fall from my face and my whole body shakes. Still the blood runs from my knee. I think about Ollie, how blunt I was with him. I frantically search for a pen in the top drawer of my kitchen cupboard and I write him a letter. I owe him this.

Dear Ollie,

I want to apologise for the last time we were together. I didn't mean the blunt words spat in your direction from my vile mouth. I'm sorry for being another person to enter your life and then leave. I appreciate how selfish this is, but I really must go. I carry too much hurt inside that I am unable to quash or house any longer.

When we first met, you made me feel safe, calm and warm. You were the light to my dark. I'm sorry I pushed you away as quickly as I let you in. I so dearly wish my mind was like what you want it to be, but it isn't and never will be. You opened the door to me and when you spoke it made sense and my insides glow.

You helped me feel alive again. You were a shelter from the storm and made me believe everything was going to be OK. When I talked you listened, you didn't judge, and I respect you for that. These last few weeks, I haven't felt so well. My mind has deteriorated. I feel so angry, frustrated and scared.

The chaos that circulates my mind needs to stop. My racing mind has this control over me and the noise in my head gets my thoughts so very muddled up. I don't have the tools to deal with the intensity of the suffering and torment I feel each day. Every minute of every day I am drowning. I am sinking from the minute I wake, and I can't keep myself above the water any longer.

I'm in so much pain, physically and mentally. It's excruciating and will only continue to grow, so I'm *choosing this way out. I can't handle the stigma and shame that stems from my self-harm. When I look at myself, I see nothing but hate. I no longer recognise myself or the person I once was. I find it so deeply unfathomable and impossible to explain what I have become, what I have done to myself and how I have ended up here, but I have.*

Taking my own life means I am finally free and, as ridiculous as this sounds, it feels like the only sensible option I have left. Whilst I will miss you, I can at least finally see my friend again and will no longer be in pain. Please don't beat yourself up or harbour any guilt, as you have no idea of my state of mind. I feel a burden to others.

The world will be no worse off without me and will continue like it always does; there is no tragedy in my departure. I need to end my suffering. I crave peace. I just want quiet. I know you would tell me I'm not alone and that we can work it out, that people care about me and this will pass and there is hope, but honestly, I don't feel there is.

You will tell me everything is forgivable, reversible and life will get better and in time I will be triumphant, stronger and win this war. The problem is, I don't have the stomach for the challenge. I don't feel ready for a battle of this magnitude. If I had a tiny ray of hope I would cling to it with both hands, but I don't. I can't possibly endure a lifetime of the hurt I house inside.

I feel weak and the wicked storm that rages over me every day makes me weaker still. I have no ability to cope. This path I choose means I can finally be at rest with the war that rages over me. This battle is too overwhelming and unbearable. I feel I am living in a world in which I don't exist.

Please forgive me; I'm sorry.
Ada XXX

I fold the note and place it on the table underneath a mug. The mug which Daisy bought me, which has the words etched on the front, "*Two friends are never apart, sometimes in distance never in heart*". Tears consume my tired eyes. I pour the remains of my cocaine onto the table then push my credit card hard on top, breaking up the congealed granules. I work frantically, chopping the lumpy powder into two large fine lines then roll a five-pound note at speed and fill each nostril with my poison.

It hurts, but it blankets and numbs the back of my throat, gums and then my teeth.

I pour a quarter litre of vodka into a large wine glass and neck it whole. Most of it sprays back up through my nose and dribbles down the front of my filthy dressing gown. As I walk to my bedroom my steps feel lighter as the cocaine rushes through my blood.

With trembling hands, I open my wardrobe door and reach up high for the thick, long, leather belt. I grab it from its hanger with haste and walk back to the hallway and quiver as I push the kitchen chair to under the hallway window. I stand upon the chair with belt in hand and tie one end around the middle iron bar. I pull on it, to ensure it will take my weight, then tighten the other end firmly round my warm, pulsating neck.

I stand on the chair. This is my final stand. I feel calmness, clarity and free of fear. I am not scared anymore; there is no reason to be. My throat hurts, so I breathe through my nose. My mind is confused and dull. I hear whispers, faint voices and mummers. I close my eyes and am transported to somewhere new. It is peculiar but peaceful. I do not recognise the faces nor the architecture. I see a choir dressed head to toe in white. High-pitched angelic voices sing, and mystical visions appear. Every bit of pain is washed away and replaced with a warm, rich, euphoric contentment that sweeps my soul.

I am now floating away and float further still until arriving in a picturesque setting where Daisy is waiting for me. I arrive at a restaurant showered with pretty white lights and she smiles as she catches my excited gaze for the first time in months.

We gallop towards one another and embrace as our favourite songs play in the background. We share a bottle of expensive pink wine to wash down our heavenly margherita pizza and put the world to rights, just like the good old days, as our bloated tummies cramp from laughter.

The waiters are tall, dark and handsome, and flirt tirelessly with us. Afternoon turns to evening and we move on to somewhere else with bright, shining lights and blissful beats, where we dance until our legs are limp and feet are sore. A waiter with big, dreamy eyes and long, muscular, tanned arms takes our cocktail order at the bar. He winks at me after he has given me my change and writes his number on the back of my receipt. We spend hours talking, having so much to catch up on, and dip our toes in the warm sea, watching in awe as the sun goes down.

I come around and reality snaps. I am back here in the most ghastly of surroundings. My whole body shakes and my wounds throb from the cocaine now surging through my system at speed. My heartbeat rushes. I look out of the window for a final time at congested London streets that my tired feet will never tread again.

This is it; my knees tremble. I struggle and attempt to kick the chair away, but I can't kick it. I'm not strong enough, but then it starts to wiggle and shift, and in a final panic I manage to do it. The chair is now removed from under me and I hang. I am choking and the belt feels like it will cut through my jaw as the cold, tough leather takes my weight. I am struggling, kicking, screaming and gasping. I lose all light and as I do Ollie walks past my window. He sees me; panic rushes over his face. He kicks the door; he kicks it twice, three times, but it won't open. I struggle; I black out.

June 26th – Ollie

I approach Ada's flat and bear witness to the most earth-shatteringly awful sound. I hear it again and then silence, an eerie, unnerving silence. I pass her hallway window and see her tormented face; it's a foul shade of purple. She looks at me, a defeated, panic-stricken portrait. I try to kick open the door but am powerless to do so. I try once more; still I struggle to break through. I try forcing my first through the small glass pane but fail miserably. In in a final fit of desperation, I kick the door open with a strength I am unaware I possessed.

She is on the floor; her body seizes, twitching, jerking erratically across the hallway floor like a fish fresh out of water. She is conscious but I am unsure of the damage caused from her suspension. Blood pours from her nose and foam froths, gathering on the right-hand side of her jittering mouth. My adrenaline is high and her life at stake.

Frantically, I remove the belt from her swelling, swollen throat. I release the tension around her thin, pulsating neck, allowing her to breathe. As the compression is loosened, she gasps, heaves, then chokes, making a sobbing wail as blood circulates back to her brain.

I call 999 and tell them she is conscious and hold her cautiously, worried I may compound her injury. I am told to remain calm and that assistance is on its way. Her pencil-thin legs twitch and shake like twigs trapped in a typhoon. On the left side of her frail neck is a cut from the belt which angles upwards towards her left ear. There is deep bruising as bulging, wicked veins show themselves in all their ghastly glory.

I lie next to her, my face just inches from hers. "Stay with me, Ada, it's going to be OK. I won't let you die."

She looks back at me with dejected, bloodshot eyes. Her pulse races. I feel her heartbeat and know she is still with me. I gently hold her cheeks. Blood continues to leak from her nose, running onto her tatty terracotta floor tiles. I try to stay calm but panic. Terror runs through me. I scream out for help and plead for the emergency services to hurry.

I look at her hollow expression as all life and colour is sucked from her face; still she whines and whimpers. She chokes again. "Don't go. Don't go, Ada, don't go." Tears fill my hands. I close my eyes and I no longer see Ada. I see demons dancing in a destitute, wicked landscape. All daylight disperses. The pain and the tears come in waves and don't stop. It is a blistering-hot morning, but I shiver. The pain I feel is so overwhelming.

Anger flares, raising his unwelcome, tormented head. I am instantly transported to the sour feeling and emotions of when Grace passed. "Where are they? Where are they? Come on!" I scream. I hold her; still she shakes, still the blood pours. She is sick; she is sick again. I call 999 again. Again, I am told to remain calm and that help is just minutes away.

I softly hold her head and wince as I gaze at her broken body. She has lacerations and tears all over. Cuts, bruises, scabs and scars line her limbs. She looks tiny. I stroke her pitch-black eyebrows and tell her that together we will get through this. Screeching sirens momentarily ease my racing mind.

The paramedics arrive and take over. I stand up at speed and run to the bathroom. Nausea strikes and clatters. It consumes me whole. I shake all over then vomit. Violent, hellish bile roars from my mouth.

As I walk from the bathroom a paramedic with a friendly face walks towards me. "Ollie?" He hands me a letter with a sympathetic look in his eye. I read it and weep. He consoles me with a warm embrace.

After several minutes Ada is taken away in an ambulance. I try to imagine how awful she must have felt to choose to leave this life using such an inhumane, gruesome path. I ponder what passed her poorly mind in those final seconds as the arteries in the neck were compressed by the belt restricting the blood to her brain.

I picture her panic and loss of consciousness due to suffocation. I visualise her personal struggle and ponder if she felt pain or perhaps enthralment by the notion of her heartbeat stopping, giving Ada the peace she so desperately craved. Egotistically, I wonder if, in those final moments, I crossed her cruel mind.

I think of her endless freefall through grief and feel so sad she was unable to appreciate the beauty she possessed. I feel confused and sorrowful that a person whose laughter could light up the darkest room could wind up in a hospital bed after attempting to take her own life.

Shockwaves run through me as I struggle to understand. I am full of self-blame, confusion and despair. I understood her struggle too well; I had these feeling after Grace passed. I thought we had enough, together as a unit, to heal our wounds and make it through to the other side. It pains me that our friendship was not enough to give her the strength to ride this out and make her want to stay.

She reached a point where her emotional reserves were burnt out. Her tiny, broken body full in capacity of both emotional and physical pain. She held out until the last minute to get help, but it was too late; it never came.

It was only I, aware of how deep her problems were, and the precarious scale of Ada's inner conflict. Her crisis and despair, so desperate and so severe. She thought she was in control; she told me she was in control. She lost control. Her fragile life tipped back and forth in an exhaustive manner, with her life finally being outweighed by the sad alternative: death.

A moment of impulsivity, a window of opportunity disrupting her precarious balance, leading Ada down the road where depression is victorious. She gave into the impulse, to the confusing, conflicting voices, clouding and muddling her murky, mucky, heavy mind. I should have been there and ensured she got the help she needed. I let her down and failed her. I feel deep and utter shame.

I open her window to air the flat. Outside the morning sun is a peculiar misty shade of pink. I feel faint. My insides are unsettled. Fear takes complete control. I close my eyes, but this just amplifies my pain.

I should have done something and should have intervened; I feel such guilt for not getting her professional help when I knew it was needed. I should have spoken up and told someone; I knew what was going on. I cringe inwardly, thinking, *Why didn't I get her the help she craved?* My mind is a grey blur, full of pain, disbelief and anger. I feel a lump in my throat, and my lips wobble. My mind goes into freefall and tears start to fall. I fall to the floor and feel as though the whole base of my life has been knocked from under my feet.

July

Ollie & Ada

I approach the hospital with apprehension as painful memories of Grace's passing come flooding back. My heart jumps and my stomach somersaults. A snowball of sadness accumulates, accelerating into an avalanche that covers me whole. I struggle to open the heavy wooden door as I walk through the intimidating, cold, bleak corridor.

My mind is instantly taken back to when Grace was being wheeled away from my grasp while I scream out in vain as our distance expanded. She left and I was on my hands and knees, frantically praying for an intervention, for anything, to cease her brisk departure. It's been over six months and I am back at this bleak, unforgiving landscape, a wicked environment where all one can wish for is good fortune.

A pretty girl with striking red hair lifts her head as my heavy footsteps startle her. "Can I help you, sir?" she asks, reluctantly removing her large green bulb-like pupils from her glaring computer screen.

I am told to take as seat as I sit in a busy waiting room where agitated families argue, wildly pointing fingers at one another as behind their desks staff look nervous, desperately trying to ensure everyone is seen to in an orderly fashion. Children scream and over-enthusiastic staff wheel whining, wounded souls on warped, wonky wheelchairs as relatives comfort and assist those weak and needy. I pick up a magazine but am unable to focus or think straight. My hands and feet shake.

After several minutes I am directed to a room. My temperature rises. My head aches and I taste my bad breath. I feel a surge of nausea. I enter the room and sit down on a small, plastic chair, as uncomfortable as Ada's vacant expression. I give her a bag full of magazines, unsure she will like them. Outside the weather begins to calm. The tapping on the window is now absent as the skies appear more gentle and mellow.

"Thank you, that's sweet of you." She looks at the floor, nervous about catching my gaze.

"How have you been?" I ask, embarrassed at the insensitivity and stupidity of my question. She fails to respond, with an uneasy look etched upon her tired face.

"I'm sorry you had to find me like that. That you had to witness that. You saved my life. I can't believe I have done this to you, to myself. I just felt so sad. I couldn't see any other way out. I got caught in the headlights and felt so lost and like I had nothing. My self-harm was unimaginable. I was so ashamed of the person I had become. My thoughts became so clouded and my mind so claustrophobic. As sad it sounds, I could only find peace and excitement from my self-mutilation," she says in a sad, quiet tone.

"You don't have to apologise or explain. I'm just sorry it came to this and that I wasn't there for you, that you felt I couldn't help and that this was your only option," I say in condolence.

"I had lost the person I once was and didn't think she was ever coming back. Each passing day, I would sink deeper and fade further and faster into the ether, away from whom I thought I was and where I wanted to be. I felt a change in me and lost all sense of self-worth, pride and sanity.

"My determination, resilience and fearlessness all withered away. I went downhill with no brakes; the walls were caving in. All I could do was shut myself away and accelerate my own demise. My depression and anxiety grew into an unmanageable force I was unable to calm. I just wanted a way out, the quickest way possible. The self-harm, the drugs and drink. It just kind of spiralled and I couldn't stop it.

"Every day felt like an endurance test, tall vast mountains I was unable to climb and navigate. I couldn't cope. I didn't have the energy, strength or desire to carry on. I just wanted an easy way out. Dying, it didn't scare me. I felt desperate, and in that moment, it felt the right thing to do. I felt there was little left to live or care for."

She looks fatigued and tired; she finally stops talking, allowing herself to breathe, and lets me talk.

"I feel so guilty. I knew what was going on and should have been more forceful in ensuring you got the professional aid you so obviously required. I should have taken the lead, then perhaps you wouldn't be where you are now. I should have helped you. I let you down, I'm sorry," I say sympathetically.

"It doesn't matter how determined you are, Ollie; regardless of your best endeavours, you can't keep someone else alive. I had tunnel vision, and it overrode my better judgement. You can't underestimate where my mind was. Everything stopped making sense. When I lost Daisy people would tell me that life goes on; I just stopped wanting mine to. I didn't want help as I didn't want someone delving into my past. I didn't want to learn about my mistakes and misdemeanours. I foolishly believed my self-harming and alcohol dependency was helping me, but it didn't block out or by-pass the grieving process; it just made everything ten times worse. I am an adult. I crossed the line and must now deal with the aftermath. I feel shame, hurt and sorrow. I've let you and myself down. Now I must live with the consequences.

"I worried it was just the start, and what if I had changed for good? I couldn't face a lifetime spent battling suicidal thoughts and always feeling on the brink of a fatal decision. It's hard work battling with a mind like mine, every minute of every day. It feels like toothache, this dull pain, and it's always there. You can't see beyond it; the pain will never end. They only way to halt the excruciating pain is to rip it out and end it."

I hold her and look deep into her eyes. I can see she is breaking, as a tear falls from her eyes.

"I promise to help and support you and be here for you when you need me. As difficult as it might be, take what positives you can and use this as the moment to turn your life around. You have hit your rock bottom; the only way is up. I knew about the cuts but could only see what's on the outside; I can't see what's going on inside. I guess you hid that part well. You need to let other people in to give you the support to get better."

"I got so lost in my grief. I was in a dark hole that was claustrophobic, full of self-loathing and pain, a place I simply wanted to escape from. The tide of depression was sweeping me away to an unhappy ending; I didn't believe that anybody would care if I was gone. I didn't think anybody would even notice. I was just in a pit of despair."

"Without you, Ollie, I wouldn't be here now. You made me feel calm. When I was crying in your arms and begging for you to let me die you saved me. You held me tight, supported me and told me you wouldn't let me die. In my darkest hour you made me feel content. When my eyes filled up, you mopped away my tears. I promise I won't let you down again," she says.

"I should have been your safety net, your protection. I can't imagine how much pain you must have been in to feel that desperate. I'm so sorry. You're still here, though, still breathing. You have been given a second chance, an opportunity for change, to do something with your life, to own it once more and, in time, be happy. Some people don't get that. Take your life, Ada, and own it. Be brave and cling to the belief that a better life is waiting for you; just hold on."

I kiss her on the cheek and tell her I will be back again tomorrow. I leave and walk pass her window as she looks at me with an almost embarrassed look etched upon her drained, weary face.

July 24th – Ada

Wild screaming breaks my sleep. It confuses my tired mind as my sleepy eyes gradually adjust to the pitch-black. I am alone; it takes several seconds for me to remember I am in North London psychiatric hospital ward. I have been here for a few weeks now. The screeching and whining from another room intensifies as the sound amplifies, scattering around the building. Owing to bed shortages and the prioritising of patients, I am informed I will be leaving in a few days.

The thought of leaving, adjusting to life outside my ward, fills me with dread. When I arrived, it felt daunting and oppressive, but I have thrived on the structure, being told when to get up and what to eat. Having my freedom taken from me at first felt overwhelming, but having it handed it back to me scares me just as much. My time here has allowed me some much-needed breathing space and perspective. I am so grateful for the support, encouragement and positive advice I have received. In truth I craved it. I have felt my inner chaos calm and every day feel marginally closer to a return to the person I once was, a person I once liked.

It won't be a relief to go home, as here I feel safe. I panic about adjustment to home life and agonise over how I will improve, get stronger, adjust and fill my time with my newfound independence. For the past few weeks, there has been somebody by my side to guide me. When I have cried, I have been listened to and offered encouragement. When panic strikes the staff have been patient. When I have felt broken someone has picked up the pieces.

I feel slightly abandoned by the hospital, by the system, and a failure for wishing I could extend my stay. Here I am surrounded by noise, by people; at home the silence scares me. I'm worried about the loneliness of recovery. I worry about my medication and sleep routine. Here I'm told when to sedate, sleep and eat; it's easy as I have help.

In the hospital I have the luxury of relying on others when my anxiety kicks in. I needed this time-out from the narcissistic, self-observed bubble in which I lived. I needed help, but I felt so small and so much of a burden and that all avenues of help were closed off for someone like me. I had lost my voice, but here, I have found it.

I want to change and am even positive about my agreed treatment plan. No longer do I have the desire to sabotage my own recovery with drinking and self-harm. I needed a safe space and change of scenery to enable me to process my grief, to give me a chance to allow my scars to heal.

I'm unsure if it is the medication, the lack of alcohol and drugs, the diet, or the sleep, but I feel like my mind is reacting in a positive manner. I feel my sadness lifting. I am progressing and my racing mind is calmer. Wicked thoughts that would once manifest themselves and the noises in my head have slowly drowned out.

I don't want to go back to square one; it's what scares me the most. My overwhelming desire to not be around any longer has passed, for now. I am scared when I leave it will return; however, there is no other option, and nowhere else for me to go. I must act responsibly in order to enhance my chances of a positive outcome, with any thoughts of pessimism shut firmly away.

I must suppress emotions I don't want to feel and be

strong. When gruelling dark depression sweeps me away and suffocates me, limiting my breathing and leaving me paralysed, breathless and endlessly weeping, I must revert to my plan.

I need to use this moment as a turning point and look to my future with a sense of hope, taking a step towards the life I wish to live. My recovery will take time. I must remain realistic. I have been given a second chance. There will be dark days ahead, but after my short stay here I feel more equipped to deal with these. I can accept that suicide was my past, but I will not allow it to define my future.

July 27th – Ada

A gutsy shower whips my windowpane. I watch as the world moves at speed whilst mine creeps along at a lumbering pace, petrified for what my future holds. I have been home for a few days now, let loose and thrown back in the lion's den. I'm overwhelmed. I sensed this would happen.

Coming home to the remnants of my failed attempt to take my life reminds me just how unwell I was; the reality check hits hard and strikes a chord with me. I have removed any objects in and around the house that I felt I could use to harm myself. I am unable to celebrate having made it through to the other side when lingering fears of a relapse loom large.

I'm told to rest, relax and let my body heal. To some, this may sound heavenly; to me, it's torture. Filling my time when suffering with mental illness I find taxing. There are moments when I lack motivation and spend hours sedated, slouched in front of a TV show I have little interest in. I stare motionless at the walls and watch as the clock appears to move anti-clockwise after another bout of medication kicks in. At other times I'm restless and feel the need to be on the move, so pace my room at a furious speed and anxiously bite my nails, feeling I could climb the walls.

With so much spare time I find myself over-analysing everything. I second-guess every negative emotion, scrutinising and dissecting each passing thought. These questions and many more continue to float around my head; it's exhausting. I cry in fear of what might become of me, concerned about my next manic episode. My troublesome, irrational mind fluctuates between feeling happy I am still here one minute and crying I'm still here the next. My discharge instructions fail to mention waking from my daily nightmares. I miss the structure of hospital.

I am exhausted, numb, remorseful and angry about what's happened. I find it hard to see hope for my future and worry I won't ever bounce back to my old self as the consequences of my actions lean heavy on my small frame. I should leave the house, do something, anything, to distract my racing mind, but I'm scared to do so. Anxiety kicks in, agoraphobia, something else to add to the list. I'm agitated and on edge. Intense, out-of-control thoughts and endless negativity wash over me, seemingly impossible to escape from.

I wait for the intenseness of these emotionally paralysing feelings to pass; I pray for them to pass, as I struggle to handle the chaos. My willingness for survival, I find tiring. I must remain positive and keep calm and remember these feelings will subside, but I am scared and petrified; the hours of loneliness eat me up inside.

I pick up my paperwork and desperately attempt to digest my safety plan, outlining what to do when I feel like this in case of an emergency, but I panic as these instructions, explained to me in what seemed like thirty seconds, mean nothing to me in my isolation and current mindset.

My heart races. I can barely feel my body. My legs have gone numb. I am now sinking deeper into what I fear is a full-blown panic attack. I try hard to focus on my breathing, but it fails to relent. I pace the room, frantically taking deep breaths to try to calm me. I pick up a colouring book and some pencils and drink a glass of water. The noises in my head accelerate into wild screams. I refer to my notes, but the words are mumbled and my mind frenzied. The voices get louder still. I push the pencil so hard into the book it causes the nib to break and smash the glass against the wall.

I panic. My body trembles as anxiety strikes, cutting me whole. I shiver and ache. All over it stings. I sweat; my breathing shortens. I fight back floods of back tears, utterly depleted by my overpowering emotions unlike anything I've ever experienced before.

July 31st – Ada

I awaken in a state of panic. I run to the bathroom and throw up blood. The rich red liquid showers against the grubby magnolia tiles as the evidence of my alcoholism, my disease, surrounds me. Pins and needles attack and my stomach cramps. I feel nauseous and am sick once more, this time a sticky, thick bile. I sweat profusely. I've lost control and am deteriorating. I'm so sick of feeling sad but lost the courage to fight back some time ago. I'm nervous, frightened, unsettled, exhausted, anxious, overwhelmed and empty. My empty fucking life revolves around this evil, wicked and unforgiving habit. No longer am I living, my life instead confined to these four walls and my racing, raging mind. Just for one day, I would so dearly love to find peace, normality and relaxation.

I stumble through another morning. I feel claustrophobic and am unsure how to live my life. I want to hide, run away and stop situating myself in circles of chaos, but having lived in the darkness for so very long I'm worried that change could blind and disorientate me and leave me more fragile than I am right now. I am scared, unable to see a way out and beyond desperate. To heal means to stop the hurt, but to stop the hurt means realisation and real life. I'm unsure if I'm ready for that.

I tell myself I must stop using cocaine and must stop drinking. *This will stop now*, I tell myself. Today will be the day it all stops. I need to stay strong. Before this thought has time to pass through my mind, my frantic hands call the dealer, my deliberation lasting as long as it takes to put my coat on and walk across the road as if my limbs have developed a mind of their own.

It's 8.25am; my dealer is late. He is always late. My shaking hands count the money once, twice and a third time underneath the shield of a jacket from the thin, driving drizzle. Eventually he arrives; I attempt to act pissed off, but it's hard to do so when his grubby mitts contain what my impatient twitching body craves. I thank him like he is giving me a heart transplant and surge into the twenty-four-hour off-licence intent on maximum self-destruction.

I pick up two heavy bottles of the cheapest gin on the shelf and tap my feet impatiently in a queue situated behind young teenage tearaways with fake IDs purchasing their morning nicotine hit. I try to balance, and, in my drunken stupor, lean against the rail housing the morning news as a handsome man with a beautiful young girl walks in. His stare startles me. Our eyes meet; still he stares as if he knows me. "Ada, is that you?" Then it hit me: it's Niall from work. I used to care how I was judged on the outside; sadly, this fear has now left me.

"Next customer, please," says the man behind the counter as I nervously place my sad, sparse shopping basket in Niall and his daughter's view. Two bottles of gin, a bottle of lemonade and a bag of ice.

"God, Ada, are you OK? What happened to you? I'm sorry, I'm so, so sorry." His voice breaks and he hugs me as his little girl looks scared and nervous of the wobbly lady with bloodshot eyes reeking of sweat, sick and booze using her dad to maintain her balance.

I place the gin back on the counter and push my shaking frame past gaggles of schoolkids as tears fill my eyes. Returning home, I go run to the bathroom. I look in the mirror as demons dance behind my eyes. I look in the mirror and I see a failure, an addict, a weak, broken, hopeless and hurting lost cause, a poor imitation of the person I once was, and I cry.

I stare into my bloodshot eyes and see my struggle. With eyes wide open, I see myself and the evil disease that has raged over me slowly shrinking the person I once was. I see a woman desperate for peace and relief and for freedom from disease. I'm angry, lost and worry if I will ever be free.

I punch the mirror glass; smithereens smash all around me and I cry. My knuckles are cut, the pain intense; it penetrates and comes in waves, deep, dark wave after wave. My insides are twisted and torn. I cry.

My life is falling apart, but inside me is someone refusing to give in. I am ready to listen. From somewhere, I don't know, I find the power to stop. I wonder if it was the intervention of Niall, a higher power, a coincidence – call it what you like. I need to take this shame, this guilt and use this moment as the moment my life turned around.

I take the phone from my pocket. I call Ollie; I scream, I sob and hyperventilate. "I give up, I surrender. I'm not going to fight this anymore. Please, help me, please."

He tells me to hold on and that he will be with me as soon as he can. I scream at the top of my voice and then black out.

The time is 2pm and I wake on the sofa, drenched in sweat. Ollie is next to me; he is with Vinnie. Vinnie passes me a glass of water from a chipped mug.

"I'm sorry, I freaked out. I had a panic attack and wasn't sure what to do, who else to call. I don't trust myself. I don't want to fail. I thought I was getting better. I want to change. I'm worried about staying safe and on track. I'm worried my dark thoughts and self-harm might return. In hospital I had started to stabilise and felt safe. Here, I don't know what to do," I say, embarrassed for my failure in being able to look after myself.

Vinnie looks at my coffee table, with some snapped colouring pencils and a meditation book on it, and gives me a sympathetic smile. "Ada, it breaks me when I look at you. I can see how vulnerable you are. There is a place, not far from here, the Reynolds Recovery Rooms, it's in Hertfordshire. After losing Sophie, I tried to take my own life. The people at the Reynolds Recovery Rooms saved me. What they did for me was nothing short of miraculous; had it not been for them, I would not be here now.

"I don't want you to get angry or upset, but I have made some calls, I know the people there; I consider them friends of mine. We are going to take you there in the morning. It's a private centre where you will feel safe and be offered the time, space and support to get better. You need professional help; the people there are trained to understand and help you. You can work through your thoughts and feelings and help find your way back in a safe space and talk openly and honestly without fear or judgement.

"You have no support network here – well, apart from me and Ollie, but what we can offer is limited. This isn't forever, but you need to get better and you can't stay here. If you do, I think we all know the conclusion. Just trust me. You need to be kind to yourself and take this opportunity. If I hadn't gone when I was pushed by a friend I wouldn't be here now. I was lucky; someone cared enough about me to ensure I went. Just like Ollie and I care for you," he says as his eyes circulate, observing my grotty flat.

"Just embrace it, hold no fear; it can't be any more terrifying than how you feel right now, can it? You need to surround yourself with professional help, trained minds who will listen to you without judgement and help you overcome this to give you the best chance possible of becoming the best version of you. I won't take no for an answer. It's voluntary, so you can leave when you want – what harm can it do? Please just try. You need to help us and pack a suitcase."

Vinnie talks slowly and calmly with sorrow drenched in his piercing eyes as if he won't take no for an answer.

"Thank you, Vinnie, thank you; I can leave anytime? Promise?"

He smiles at me; it warms me while I cry quietly in relief as my sobbing halts and panic retracts. Ollie hugs me and tells me it's going to be OK.

August

Ada

I take a deep breath after deep breath. Everything throbs. Tears fall the length of my withered, blushing cheeks. I feel embarrassment and deep shame. Ollie is in the back of the taxi sat to my left, tightly holding my hand, as Vinnie sits to my right. I stare out the window and aimlessly gaze, jealous of every passer-by as sheets of vicious rain pelt and bounce from the car windscreen.

I fear what's coming. I imagine padded cells, straitjackets and inmates so delirious they shuffle instead of walking, drooling and dribbling as they try to speak. I envisage rusty barbed wire over twelve-foot brick walls and a security guard sat in a watch tower with a rifle ready to shoot, and nurses armed with handcuffs, tear gas and batons, ready to pounce at the slightest eye contact.

After what seems an eternity the driver hits the

indicator and makes a sharp left turn and then I see it, in big bold letters: "The Reynolds Recovery Rooms". The building is bigger than I anticipated; it is gleaming white and modern. Ollie helps me out of the car. He hugs me; I kiss his unshaven cheek and collapse into his arms. We walk through the large, red entrance door and take a seat.

The three of us gaze up at the ceiling, not a single word is uttered in fear of saying the wrong thing. The pale thin girl on reception breaks the silence. "Can I help you?"

Vinnie talks to her, then a few other people come over, recognising him. They embrace and shake hands then he points to me. I stare at the floor, feeling vulnerable, weak and awkward.

"I just need you to complete these forms, please. We are going to check you in now. I will call Kim; she will be down in a minute. You are in safe hands. It's time to say your goodbyes."

I feel drained and my breathing is awkward, but I try my best not to break, and mumble dishonest words in Ollie and Vinnie's direction. I tell them I am OK and wear a strong, stern portrait on my face, doing my best to keep myself composed, while inside I'm crumbling as quickly as pastry.

Ollie leans down and gently holds my shoulders. He leans forward and kisses my left brow. "You are going to be OK. Should you need us we are only down the road. It's going to be OK."

I break and Ollie consoles me. I find comfort in his warmth. He stares for an age, as if this is his final glance. Vinnie holds out his left hand and when I shake it, he uses his other arm to tightly take the weight off me; he brings me closer towards him. He holds me tighter still to cease my shaking.

Ollie and Vinnie leave; it breaks me. I'm jealous of their freedom, but I know where I will end up should liberty be handed back to me. They leave and I'm alone. My road is paved with fear. I just want to feel normal, complete and content; I want my insides to sparkle and shine and replace this void. I feel I am narrowly dangling by a thread above a dark void. My withered frame is close to collapse; it wants me to fall, to fail and give in, but I must keep holding on. I must keep strong.

Minutes later Kim arrives. I hear her before I see her, her high heels clattering around the corner. She wears a large smile, a loud, coloured dress and talks at speed. "No need to look so nervous; you are going to be just fine. This is a great place. It will be OK, I promise." She says in a Nigerian accent as her strong perfume bites the back of my throat.

I am taken a few hundred metres down a gleaming white corridor until we arrive at a door on which Kim softly knocks. A short gentleman with a big smile greets us.

He is as wide as he is tall and the buttons on his blue shirt look ready to pop. He is bald on top with slicked-back silver hair above each ear. He reaches out his hand to shake mine; he smiles and then speaks. "You must be Ada? I am Neville; do come in."

I sit fidgeting, rocking on a cold, hard chair, biting my nails. Neville takes a big gulp from his small glass of water and looks at my skinny, milky, scarred and withered arms.

"Right OK, then, first things first. Everyone here has been admitted voluntarily, so nobody is forcing you to stay. You haven't been detained; your freedom and liberty are not taken away; you are free to leave now, though I wouldn't recommend it." He laughs and looks at me, waiting for a reaction. I choose instead to look at the floor, nervous, dishevelled and sad.

Neville goes through my file. We discuss my history, my care plan and the various medications I will be prescribed to aid my recovery. He talks of a change of diet, sleeping patterns and group therapy.

"Our brain, just like any other part of our bodies, can get sick from time to time. We can't help you if you aren't honest. Being here could save your life, but ultimately it depends on you and you alone. You will only get out of this what you put into it. We will help you, but you need to let us help you; approach this with an open mind, be willing and have faith in the programme and it will work – trust me.

"You are not alone; we are there with you every step of the way through your journey to recovery. What you are going through is life-altering. You will, of course, have moments when you might question the programme and doubt the benefits of being here, but you must remain positive and believe there is hope for change.

"Recovery takes time, both physically and emotionally. What you are going through is a daunting experience, but you can regain control; you will gain control. You can find your way back to a life filled with hope and a new sense of purpose and meaning. Think of your stay here as a short-term step towards a better life; each small step is a great leap forward. Being here is extending your life. Take each day as a new day. Whilst there is a temptation to place too much energy and importance on the days, weeks and months in advance, just deal with today. Stay positive, believe in the programme and believe in yourself."

He takes another large gulp of his water and hands me a book. Nervously I take it from his grasp.

"This is the Big Book. It contains the twelve steps that are the core of the Alcoholics Anonymous programme. It is a programme has helped hundreds and thousands of men and women overcome addiction and offers the best chance for long-term recovery. There is no race. There is no rush. It is step work. Following these steps offers a chance to give you back control and put you on the right path, where you will find healing, hope, freedom and ultimately recovery.

"These steps outline how to recover from compulsive, out-of-control behaviours and restore manageability to one's life. The twelve steps will change your life should you choose to embrace them. The journey will take you from a path of despair and disconnection and provide you with peace and fulfilment.

"For each step there will be an exercise I will need you to complete. All the paperwork is here in the file. These steps, your programme, will predominately be done in a group; however, there is also lots of work that can be completed in isolation. There is a great deal of work to be done. The pursuit of happiness and freedom should be exciting. Take back the life that was given to you and give yourself a chance for a better outcome. Give yourself the happy ending that you deserve, free of stress, upset, torment and sadness. Embrace change and don't be scared. Believe in the positivity of hope and recovery and that there is a different road and this one leads to a happier place than the one you currently tread.

"You must be open and willing to change. I promise we will break and untangle these patterns and self-destructive cycles. We need to redirect your energy to a new way. We are going to apply these steps to your self-harm, alcohol and drug dependency. Whilst challenging and hard work, it will be life-altering.

"OK, so rules: there are no drugs, no alcohol and no abusive behaviour. We ask that you treat others how you would wish to be treated. Should you choose to violate any of these rules, you will be sent home. There are no second chances. This is a new start, a new day and a new chapter in your life. Today is where your life begins. There is a daily structure you will be expected to follow; the plan is in your pack and Kim can talk you through this. If you need anything don't hesitate in asking; my door is always open."

I shake Neville's hand then follow Kim through a few corridors until eventually we arrive at a door with the number thirty-four on. The room is clean and simple. There is a bed, a skinny wardrobe and small chest of drawers. Everything is magnolia. There is a chair and desk. There is a small bathroom with a shower, toilet and hand basin all crammed into the area, just large enough to allow the door to open.

Kim passes me a lever arch file and removes a document which highlights my times and dates for various therapy sessions.

"After breakfast each morning will be a short meditation class. This will be followed by a group therapy led by a counsellor or therapist. Late afternoon there will be other therapies, including one-on-one sessions. In addition to this we offer alternative therapy, art, music, dance and exercise programmes which you are free to participate in. Once you have made yourself at home, I will let you know the times and locations, as it can change each week dependent on demand.

"You will have a few hours of free time in the afternoon where you can make the most of some of the activities we have, or some patients choose to use their free time reading in the small library we have which isn't far from here. Bedtime is encouraged to be at a reasonable hour." She passes me a glass of water and some pills. "The medication may have potential side effects, but there are very few and they are usually only temporary and manageable. Try to get some rest; I will be back to check on you in a few hours." She shuts the door. I am alone. I drink the water and swallow the pills.

A wicked gust gathers pace inside me. Howling, ghastly ghosts wail; their hollow, blank expressions haunt me. I feel stretched to the limits of both emptiness and sorrow. I am tired beyond belief. Crowds of thoughts sweep along with nowhere to go and nobody or nothing to stop them. I drink what remains of the water; my perished throat eases, my thirst quenched. I feel faint. I struggle for words, for breath. The bright lights startle me. I close my eyes. I am exhausted and zapped of all energy.

The bleak outlook grows ever closer and all that darkens my mind suffocates me further. I close my eyes and I am falling. There is utter silence. Tears hit my cold pillow. The tablets kick in and the pain has faded to a numbness. All over just numb. My heart slows, my hands and legs stop shaking, and my fears float away.

Pins and needles dance the length of my forearm, awaking me abruptly. My heart races. I stare out the window as flocks of birds circulate; pretty patterns of symmetric black tiny dots move in swarms from left to right. I am nervous and hyper, boiling hot, then freezing cold. I clench my fists. My knees knock together and panic rears his mischievous self. Sweat sweeps through me. My hands are clammy; my heart beats faster, then faster still.

My hands tremble. Anxiety sweeps over me; my throat tightens. I gasp for air. I want to scream but I can't. I get in bed; the duvet covers me whole. It protects me. It shields me from the pain, the loneliness, my sterile surroundings. My body lurches, whimpers and shakes. I close my eyes; bright, beaming colours circulate, glorious orange shades, deep red daggers and bolts of yellow lightning. Isolation has a powerful impact on my mind. My mind is confused and dull.

The room is quiet. I lie motionless. Time ceases to exist. My head is all over the place. I feel like I have been here for months; it has not even been a week. I worry I will become too dependent on my medication. I worry it will change me for good. I worry about everything. I know I need to get better, but I don't want to change into someone different. I stand and slowly walk to the bathroom. I turn the shower on. It is hot, too hot, but the burning excites me.

Mid-morning and Kim knocks on my door, startling me. The noise is a thankful diversion from the list of agendas, my programme I am having difficulty in digesting.

"How are we doing today?" Before I have time to answer she continues talking. "I am going to the lounge now, come." Reluctantly, I agree and follow her, traipsing a few steps behind.

After a few minutes we arrive at the large communal lounge, the walls painted a sickly butterscotch colour. In the middle of the room are three big armchairs in front of a large flat-screen TV. To the left-hand side is a plywood table with some board games and jigsaw puzzles stacked high. Kim guides me to the room then walks away, singing to herself.

I take a seat. A few minutes later a lady walks in and stares at me. There are a few other people, but her attention is focused solely on me. She looks strong, powerful and has big shoulders. Still she stares. She has dark, unblemished skin with high cheekbones. She is tall and wears a tatty trilby hat and bright braces. Her fingernails are dirty, and she walks with her feet outwards like a penguin.

"Sorry, love, but you need to move." She has an oval face with sharp blue eyes that sparkle when she speaks. I ignore her and look round her large frame, maintaining my glare on a morning chat show I have not the slightest interest in.

"Hey, I am talking to you. I said you are going to have to move. You are in my chair."

Her face is now in mine; she talks in a cockney accent. I taste the stale coffee and cigarettes on her breath; her face becomes more screwed-up and agitated as each second passes.

She scares me, but I can't let her know this. "I didn't see anybody's name on it. Sit on the sofa," I say nervously, doing my best to stand my ground, observing that other people are now looking at us.

"I don't like the sofa; I like the chair. It's my chair, and you are in it," she hisses.

Kim comes over to diffuse the situation. "Ladies, am I going to have to call security? Ellie, just please sit somewhere else. Ada, stay where you are, love. Worse than a bunch of teenagers, you lot, honestly."

Ellie tuts loudly, walks to the sofa, sits down and continues to stare at me.

I feel weak and need to eat. Kim takes me to the canteen. We walk down a long, thin corridor. I hear it before I see it. Cutlery clangs and kettles boil. There are more people than I expected. Nervously I take a seat, worried it could belong to someone else. After a few minutes she returns with a tray carrying fresh orange juice and two slices of lightly buttered seeded brown toast.

"If you are after something more glamorous there is a hot food counter. Eggs, bacon, sausages, you name it – and don't worry about Ellie; her bark is worse than her bite. She is a gentle giant." The tea is too milky and the toast undercooked, but I pay no mind.

I have been back in my room for a matter of minutes when a knock on the door startles me. It's Ellie. She holds out her hand and smiles. "I'm sorry about earlier – bad morning. I am in the room next door. OK to come in?"

Ellie spends the next hour talking; I say very little.

"I try to suppress my sorrow through a cocktail of alcohol, self-harm and drugs, but nothing works; it just makes me feel worse. I had my last line of cocaine in the taxi that brought me here to keep the rising panic at bay.

I want to stop, but I'm an addict; I can't stop. My husband made it clear: fail to complete this programme and I am no longer welcome in the family home. I need to do this. I need to get better."

Her shaking hand pulls a picture from her purse. She shows me a picture of her daughters. Her face is one of pride when she talks about them. When she smiles, her well-formed white teeth brighten her whole face. She tells me that apart from her children her three favourite things are Northern Soul, dancing and painting, in that order.

She talks at ease about her battle with self-harm, her inner demons and scary characters from her past, and bats not an eyelid when recalling horrific situations she has found himself in.

She finishes talking, stands and puts her hat back on, then leaves. "If you ever need someone to talk to, you come and see me." She leaves and I feel better for talking.

August 11th

Ellie and I walk through a maze of the bright white corridors until arriving at the group therapy session which takes place in the west wing of the building each morning. The room is compact, the walls a brilliant white and the sofas made from wicker, with lavender-coloured cushions scattered upon them.

Classical music fills the air. There is the faint sound of strings being plucked and piano keys being struck. The group starts and I look around. There are ten other people present. The music stops and the speaking starts. Our group of ten is split into two groups, each group with a qualified counsellor. In my group there is Ellie; we move around the room introducing ourselves. Ellie stands and takes a deep breath.

"Cocaine is such a disgusting, lonely drug. There is no glamour, glory or pride in sitting in a hotel room in isolation with blood coming out of one nostril and the other so blocked and broken and scabbed, full of cut-up street drugs that the only way to get high is to pour the drug into your drink or push the bitter fragments into your gums; at times I would end up just eating it.

"It's Monday night and instead of tucking my children into bed and reading them a story I am in a hotel in Shoreditch tucking into three grams of cocaine. I have come here because I cannot bear for anyone to see me like this. I barricade myself in the room and work my way relentlessly through the first two grams within a few hours. The rush is almost unbearable, the desire to never come down forces me to take more. I know that this is all wrong, but I don't care. I can't stop. I won't stop.

"With shaking, nervy hands I unwrap the final gram and finish this with ease. I drink the remains of the gin in a singular gulp and then call room service. There is a knock at the door, but by this point I am too paranoid to answer it. I ignore the banging and instead focus my attention on knocking back the remains of miniature spirit bottles housed within my handbag. The cocaine and alcohol may have gone, but they rage vigorously inside me. My heart beats ferociously and then the voices start. I hallucinate and engage in dialogue with people that aren't there. My paranoia soars and I hide in the bathroom and lock the door.

"The voices grow louder; I am now being shouted at and am unable to cope. In a regrettable rage I grab the scissors from my bag. My hands are trembling with such force I am unable to break my tough, cold skin, then finally I manage it. The blood comes and I feel that release. I sit and I cry. I mop my blood with a towel, my heart races faster and I sit; I cry. I take Valium. I pass out.

"Being an alcoholic and drug addict turns you into a compulsive liar; I lie about everything and to everyone. Money, where I have been and where I am going. I even lie to my children. Your mind plays tricks on you. Eventually you start to believe your own lies. Then there is the arguing, the intense, ferocious arguing.

"Your warped mind will have you believe the reason you feel like this and the reason you are arguing is because of the normal things, the day-to-day, the kids, husband or work. In your mind the drug is never the problem. You can't blame the drugs, that's too personal; blame everything else, but don't you dare talk down to those lovely drugs.

"I'm so sick of being that person. This is my last chance. Every day is a battle. I just want a peaceful, happy existence. I just want to be happy. I want to be a good mum and make my children proud."

Ellie stops talking as tears fill her eyes. I embrace her and the group claps.

The group finishes. Ellie and I head back to the canteen. I get a bowl of tomato soup, two bread rolls and a glass of water. Eating is a struggle, but I manage to do so. It makes my stomach warm. It makes me feel marginally better. Ellie joins me in my room, we play chess and I lose three times on the trot.

I am more tired than I thought possible. Kim arrives and gives me the now-standard large, sharp-edged handful of tablets and a cold glass of water. Nausea darts through me. Wave after wave. I sit down. I start to shake and shiver. Closing my eyes, strange shapes and a collage of dark, twisted colours appear. At a certain point my eyes close and I fall asleep.

August 19th

Raging, wild nightmares wake me. Unwelcome, ferocious voices taunt me. Outside the heavens pour. I think about Daisy and how I have let her down. I think about Ollie and how I will never be good enough for him. I don't deserve him. I think about Vinnie and how foolish he was to waste his time and money on me when everything I touch turns to muck. The one consistent in my life, my ability to let down those I care for. I think about all the things I am yet to achieve and all the things I will never become. I look at my surroundings. This is where I am. This is who I am. I better get used to it.

I close my eyes and I am with Daisy; we are ice skating at Hyde Park. She is multi-tasking, skating and drinking mulled wine, trying to impress the guy who has been looking at her all evening, doing her utmost to look elegant and graceful on thin ice whilst safeguarding her drink from staining her white mink coat.

She ups her pace; her measured skating speeds up. She is now skating so fast her body is not able to keep up with the speed of her Bambi-like legs. She can't stop and there is no handrail in sight, and she flies up in the air, landing on her backside, much to the amusement of the gentleman decked in tweed. I think about Daisy, the good days when we sought no other.

Our time together passed too quickly, each minute, each hour eaten alive at such furious speed. There were never any dramas, just dreams, our only immediate concern how to stop our day from slipping away. The sky always seemed so bright.

Now my days are dismal and each step a slumbering slog. I look around my room and sit in silence. I'm banished to this dark road with no freedom to roam. I call out her name. There is no response. I scream and I shout, but any form of reply evades me. Anger rears his sorry face. I miss her so very much.

Fear washes over me. I want to escape. I am too tired. I want to run. I am too weak. I want to hide. There is no cover. A storm blows up in my mind. I am consumed by the panic and fear, and it won't leave. I feel colder; I shake. My muscles twitch; I struggle for breath. There is no light at the end of my tunnel.

The time is just after six. Outside the vicious weather barks against my pane. Driving rain beats and bangs. Dark thoughts gain momentum. Round and round like a burning ring of fire. I look around my room. I need to leave. I feel sick, claustrophobic and paranoid. Paranoid this medication is a plot to twist my mind and keep me here. I won't let them do this. I chuck on the first clothes I can find and try to open the window, but it won't budge, the gap only large enough to let air in. To where I am going, I do not know, but it must be better than this. I turn around to catch a final glimpse of the room, dearly hoping it is my last.

I keep my head down and walk through winding corridors until I reach the back door. Opening the door, my heart quickens. For the first time in days I feel excitement. I open the door and cold, bitter air bites my cheeks as hard rain lashes my face. The morning darkness has yet to lift. The air is thick; the fog sticks to me and lingers, making it hard to map my route. My socks and plimsolls are drenched; they squelch as I traipse and trudge through sodden earth, pulling away further from my lodging as the hospital lights fade to a tiny dot.

My hair is soaked and legs feel like jelly. I feel my bones creek and clatter. I find a shelter underneath thick branches and blankets of leaves. Against the thick stub of a tree, I lean back. My teeth chatter and my knees shake. I find a fallen tree branch and settle my side on this. It is damp with dew, but it matters not. I close my eyes; calmness washes over me. I have found peace and serenity. I should go back. I will be asked to leave otherwise. I think about the shame and how Vinnie will react, but I stay. For the first time in days I feel at peace and free. Alone, I close my eyes and am transported back to our bench. I talk to Daisy.

"Hi, mate, me again. I just wanted you to know I miss you. I'm sorry I let you down and ended up here. I was thinking about you earlier, about us. I love you. I miss you more than you will possibly know."

I close my eyes and cry. I am lost in my tears, my eyes are closed and my mind is swirling. A tap on the shoulder startles me, bringing me round; it's Ellie.

"You OK, love? What are you doing out here? I saw you leave, so I followed."

She removes her navy Adidas tracksuit top and wraps

it round my shaking, narrow shoulders. Instantly I feel warmth and comfort. She wraps her warm, heavy arms around my cold, shivering skin. The bleak becomes slightly brighter and my insides calm.

"I just needed to breathe some fresh air and to have some time to think. I have these lucid dreams, they merge into my consciousness, my reality, and I can't breathe. I hear these voices in my head; this black mist consumes me, and it's so strong it takes my breath away and knocks me to the floor. Perhaps I'm just not cut out for this."

Ellie looks at me and wipes the falling tears from my freezing face. "I'm not letting you leave, you know that, right? I'm not going to let that happen, not on my watch. How's about we get back inside? Get a coffee, have some breakfast and talk about this over a game of chess. I know you are scared, we all are, but running away isn't going to improve things. You've got to show some courage, girl. Light that fire in your belly. You are strong enough; I know you can do this. You feel like this because you realise the need for change, I get it, but life doesn't have to be a vicious cycle of pain and misery. You can be happy, we all can, we just have to have hope and believe in change, but the only person who can make that change is you."

I look into her eyes and trust what she is saying. Her words come from a sincere place. She is not just paying me lip service and talks with truth, care and honesty. She tightens her arms around me still. "It will get easier, I promise." I hug her and instantly feel much better.

September

Ollie & Ada

My taxi pulls to a shuddering halt. I feel my palms beginning to sweat and have a sickly feeling inside me. It happens each time I arrive here at her resting place. I thank my driver, pick up the bouquet of flowers for Grace and cautiously walk through the ancient, rusting, wrought-iron cemetery gates.

I worry perhaps I don't come here as often as I should do but have stopped beating myself up about this; I had to. I now only come here when it feels right, when I have the urge to do so, like this morning. I know that Grace is looking down on me and is aware of my feelings for her, and my frequency of visits is not a barometer of the place she holds so dearly in my heart.

The morning mist creeps over the graveyard. As far as the eye can see there is a jumble of crumbling gravestones with no two the same size or shape. It's eccentric and unique.

There are no gleaming white, perfectly polished headstones rising from manicured lawns housed within a neat and tidy picketed fence, but I like it like this and think Grace would too. Though some look new, with smooth, marble headstones and freshly laid floral tributes, most are unkempt and overgrown, with sprawling wild weeds and mould covering the engravings dedicated to the dead whose loved ones have long since stopped visiting.

I pass a young couple dressed head to toe in black. I know their pain all too well, the fresh and unforgiving crippling sadness, sorrow, anger and grief. I watch helplessly as they sob, broken-hearted. I look on and wince as they wail in unison in front of a gathering of plastic toys on top of a small grave. It's raw and it's harsh.

I walk towards Grace's resting place and nod at the groundskeeper I wonder if he notices how my visits have become more infrequent. I pass other mourners and nod at them without saying a word, a nod of sorrow, a language of the grieving. My heart accelerates as I pass each stone under a cloudless sky. There is dew on the grass and the fresh air bites my nose. I walk a narrow pathway, my cold feet wading through fallen autumn leaves, passing centuries-old shabby, weathered headstones, until finally I reach her, arriving at Grace's stone and the tiny space carved just for her.

I crouch down, removing the wet grass, sticky clumps of moss and golden-browned frosted leaves in front of her headstone, and place these in a carrier bag. I then sweep the dirt and mud from her stone. I replace her previous flower arrangement with the new flowers I have recently purchased and softly lay them, watching as their bright, blushing rosy heads fall towards her headstone.

I caress the damp corner of her concrete stone with my cold fingertips and imagine it is her face I am stroking; the touch of the stone on my skin offers me some peace as I release my tears into the cold morning air.

"Hi, it's me. Sorry I haven't been here in a while. Foolishly I believed keeping my distance would protect me and help me from feeling the hurt I housed inside. I felt scared coming here. I was petrified of the silence, of our one-way conversation, and waiting for the lump in my throat, the dry lips and the tears that would inevitably follow. Being here made your passing feel that much more cemented.

"I now understand what a privilege and honour it is to be here. The last time I was here I wasn't in the best frame of mind. I made a promise to myself that the next time I came here I would be a better version of me who was talking to you, one that you could respect.

"When you died my dreams did too. The future that we had mapped out, it was torn and twisted and all that remained was a box of photos. I lost all direction and desire to face the world. Everything I knew was gone. I was so self-absorbed and unable to pick myself up. I would wake in the night, convinced I could hear your stupid giggle, then look at your vacant side of the bed and think you would be back soon, but you were gone and were never coming back. I'm so scared of my memory of you fading and you becoming a blur. Some days I forget the tone of your voice and listen to the voicemails you left on my phone.

"I blamed myself. I was your husband and allowed you to die. You were so kind and brave. I was unable to process how someone like you could be taken from me. How someone so special could be dealt this hand and allowed to pass away. It all happened so quickly. I didn't know how to cope, what to do or where to turn. I lost all purpose and self-worth. I had no reason to do anything or no reason not to do anything.

"I was left to my own devices. There was no one to pull me up and question my behaviour. There were no rules and no regulations. Time and day became irrelevant; life just became one big mish-mash of overwhelming pain, hurt and suffering. I had these uncontrollable waves of anger, and the only way to get through the day, I am ashamed to say, was with alcohol, the one thing I promised you I would not do. I harboured such sadness and anger and became someone I didn't recognise. I was a representation of me which would have brought shame on you, but then eventually something clicked, and I picked myself up. I had no right to mope and wallow in self-pity when you rarely complained about anything.

"I miss talking to you; I miss everything. I still do. You taught me so much; I'm still learning from you. Each passing day you continue to inspire me to become a better person. I will forever be indebted to you. I just want you to know I'm here and always will be.

"I have tried to keep the flat how you like it. I still read your handwritten instructions on how to work the washing machine. I have slowly started to sort out your clothes. I wasn't sure there was ever going to be a right time to do so, but gradually I am getting there. You always moaned how you never had any shoes to wear – well, I managed to fill two bin bags. Work has been good; I started going back part-time a few weeks ago and have been doing some bits from home, enough to make sure the bills get paid. You may struggle to believe this, but I have finally started using that gym membership you got me for my birthday."

I stop babbling and take a deep breath, conscious to address the elephant in the room, and I wait patiently for my words to come. There is a tingling in my arms and my voice becomes quieter.

"Grace, there is something I feel I must tell you; it isn't easy but has been playing on my mind. I need to be honest to both you and I. I have met someone. Her name is Ada. I don't know what it is, where it will lead or what will happen, I don't even know how to describe it, but there is a connection. I understand if you feel I have let you down; if truth be told, I'm so confused about the right thing to do.

"Ada has suffered her own loss too. She has her own issues, but we are helping each other as best we can. She isn't a replacement for you but someone I have felt drawn towards. I am finding this hard, as you were always so thoughtful, respectful and kind. It feels like right now I am the opposite of each of those things."

My crackling voice breaks; I feel the tears itching and burning behind my eyes. There is a silence, an almost awkward moment as I stare at her cold, hard slab of stone with a face of guilt and shame. I am now holding her stone against my chest and again I tell her how sorry I am.

Beside me is an elderly man who sits on a bench opposite his wife's grave. He tells me his name is Walter. He pulls a flask from his bag. The smell of coffee runs up my nostrils.

"They might be gone, but they'll always be in our thoughts. You never get over it; you just adapt to it. Me and my Beatrice were married for forty-nine years. She was my ray of sunshine. One minute they are there, the next they're gone, but the love remains. It's been a year, but it still feels like yesterday when I was lowering her body into the ground. Although now separated, she is still alive in my thoughts.

"She was my first love, and she will be my last. Someone whom I shared things with that I don't want to share with anyone else. I still wear my wedding ring. It feels a betrayal to take it off entirely. I can't part with it, not just yet.

"One morning I woke, and she was next to me; it was odd, as she was always the first up. I tried to wake her, but I couldn't. I attempted CPR and an ambulance was called, but there wasn't anything they could do.

"I made her a promise on her deathbed I would never leave her on her own. That's why I come here. She didn't like the cold or the dark. I can't let her down. Coming here gives my day purpose and meaning. It might not be everyone's cup of tea, but I'm not sure what else I could do or where else I would go. I like being here and find comfort in the safety of the cemetery, away from the noise and the chaos of the world that sits outside these gates. For me, there is no place quite like it. I can contemplate things without being disturbed.

"The cemetery is a peaceful place, to think, reflect and regain perspective. A place to connect with Beatrice's spirit, to talk to her and tell her that I love her and always will. I can think of her, talk to her and ask her for guidance; I find a tranquillity, a sense of connection, and I like the way time seems to almost stand still.

"I come here to pay my respect and remember. I can't bear the separation of being in my flat on my own. Watching our TV shows on my own. I used to laugh so much and find humour in everything, but things don't seem so comical in isolation. Being here steadies me, keeps me focused and ensures my final days have some worth.

"Some folk will tell you that the past is the past; I don't believe that. I come here to honour Beatrice, who she was and all she did for me. Sometimes I find it so hard to fathom how a cold, hard stone can be all that is left to represent her when she was full of life and spirit. Maybe it was just her time.

"People might think I am mad, spending my days here talking to a bag of bones, but I know she can hear me. One day I will find out. When I meet her, she will thank me for keeping her company; I know she will. Sometimes I come here for me, not her. I'm here so I can feel close to her again, feel her warmth and feel her love once more. I need to talk to her, and this is the only way. All we can do is remember and reflect. I know Beatrice is no longer with me, but her soul is still alive.

"Coming here is a way of taking care of her and still being with her. I'm too old to get a hobby. I tell her about the day-to-day and I always feel better after seeing her. I am not a spiritual person, but in this space, I feel a connection to her. I find peace and solace in the moments spent remembering.

"I think back to how often I passed this place and it meant nothing to me, and then when Beatrice died it felt like the fiercest place on earth and now it's like my second home. What am I going to do at home all day? I might as well talk to Beatrice as talk to myself. I don't want for much; all I pray for each night now is that when my time comes, she is waiting for me and takes me by the hand so that we can live here side by side. I would like that."

He comes closer and reads the dates on Grace's headstone. "You poor thing. She was no age." He puts his arms around me and gives me a hug. I embrace his warmth and hold him tight.

I mop my tears with my sleeve and talk.

"I came here today because I needed to come clean.

"When I lost Grace, I thought I'd never want to find love again but ended up making friends with a lady called Ada. She'd lost her best friend around the same time I lost Grace. It felt good to talk to someone who was in the same boat. I missed having a partner, someone to talk to. After a few months of getting to know Ada my feelings began to change; we had things in common and, without realising it, our relationship quickly progressed. I wasn't looking for anything or anyone; it just happened. I hadn't expected to feel like that again.

"I feel guilty, like I am Grace letting down, and question if I am doing the wrong thing. I worry that what I am doing is almost inappropriate and I am defacing her memory. I feel like I have only recently accepted she has gone. I felt so much blame, anger and disbelief, confusion and guilt. I worry I'm betraying the person I lost and question if I am ready for this. I feel conflicted by the idea that I am enjoying new experiences at the expense of Grace's life. What if I am jumping in too quickly?"

"I understand, but you can't keep looking back; it does you no good. If being here can teach you one thing, it is that time is so very precious. One day we will all be forgotten; it's sad but true. Grace will always be a presence in your life. She will never, ever be forgotten while you live.

"Meeting someone else does not lessen your love for your wife. As long as you keep coming here and maintain that relationship with Grace, your guilt, in time, will soften. Some people can live a whole lifetime without finding love once; if you happen to find it twice then good on you, mate, is what I say. If this were the other way around and you had departed and your wife had the possibility of a new relationship, I'm sure you would be happy for her. You can't control your heart. You can love more than one person in your lifetime."

"It just never occurred to me that one day I would have to look for a new partner; it wasn't part of the plan."

"You have done nothing wrong, young man, and shouldn't be so hard on yourself. I'm quite sure she will forgive you and understand. She would have no reason to feel bitter or aggrieved. You shouldn't feel bad about putting yourself first.

"Just because you feel ready to receive love from a new person, it doesn't mean you're forgetting the person who has departed. It's never about moving on, only about moving forward. It is possible to carry and honour the love of the person that's died and have space in your heart to expand and love another. It's possible to move forward without forgetting and respecting your past.

"Just take it slowly and see what happens; if you don't dip your toe in the water you will never know. Life's too short to harbour regrets. Take it from an old duffer like me. It's not easy to open your heart to love again, but if it feels right then go with it; only you know how you truly feel. I'm too long in the tooth to try again, but you are a young man. Don't be upset about the things you never got to do with Grace; be thankful for the things you did get to do."

I thank Walter, stand up and leave. I feel emotionally drained but lighter and happier, like a weight has been lifted from my shoulders.

September 4th – Ada

The battle with my inner self is constant. I am in a war zone each day, but I have more energy to fight back this time. No longer do I feel the need for self-harm, alcohol or drugs to be at ease. Being in this bubble, sheltered from the outside world, has given me a safety net and time to heal. I have been here four weeks and feel a shift inside me. The longer I am here, the further away I feel from the person who arrived.

I weep most days but have also started to laugh again and feel the faintest glimmer of the person I would like to be. For the first few weeks I harboured this deep sense of frustration and questioned why I wasn't better yet – if anything, I had started to feel worse – but that has lifted. Physically and mentally I sense a change. I feel a little sharper. I don't want to fall back into a deep depression or shelter underneath substances anymore. I have started to remove the barrier I built up in self-defence and have stopped being so hard on myself.

I accept and understand I have an illness but have let go of things I kept contained for so long. My life felt like an endurance test, a rollercoaster that I longed to get off. When

I arrived, it felt so daunting. I felt like a small fish in the large sea. I sense a change within me; my lows aren't what they once were. A large part of me didn't even want to get better because getting better meant facing up to real life. I enjoyed wallowing in my own self-pity; only now am I able to appreciate just how ill I was.

I get dressed and walk the kitchen, where I have a bland bowl of cereal and back-to-back coffees that make my insides jitter and jangle. I return to my room, sit at my desk and open the book. I have been putting it off for days now. Each morning, each evening I feel guilt that I am yet to throw myself into this, sub-consciously frightened to do so.

Most of what I have heard about the twelve steps is based around a belief in God. I don't have that belief and never will. Regardless of what I have heard in my group therapy up to this point, I struggle to understand how the twelve steps can work for me.

I am an atheist. I only believe in God when I pray because I want something. I worry the twelve steps are unrealistic and over-ambitious, but what other options do I have?

Step 1
We admitted we were powerless over our addiction,
that our lives had become unmanageable.

I must accept my addiction is beyond my control and my way of doing things simply isn't working. My addiction has the power. My addiction has control. I have lost power. I have lost control.

To end the chaos, carnage, sorrow and sadness I must believe in change and that a new start is possible. My self-harm, alcohol and drug dependency is making my life and the lives of those around me difficult. My current life is not working or giving me the happiness I desire.

My alcohol consumption sets me on a path to drugs which quickly accelerates to self-harm. It is a pattern I must break. I am powerless and have lost control. I think back to the numerous episodes of self-generated chaos and battles with my inner self which I always lose. The devil always wins. I must re-group, learn and arm myself with the correct tools to defeat my dark thoughts the next time they strike. I lost the power and lost control, but I can reclaim it. I will be victorious. I believe in change and believe in hope.

My life is unmanageable. It is why I am here. As simplistic as it sounds, there is a problem and it needs fixing. I refer to Neville's notes. I must write down "I am powerless, I've lost control" ten times like a disobedient schoolchild. I write the sentence as instructed, each passing sentence becoming harder.

> I am powerless, I've lost control.
> I am powerless, I've lost control.
> I am powerless, I've lost control.
> I am powerless, I've lost control.
> I am powerless, I've lost control.
> I am powerless, I've lost control.
> I am powerless, I've lost control.
> I am powerless, I've lost control.
> I am powerless, I've lost control.
> I am powerless, I've lost control.

I regurgitate the lines over and over. I must then write down ten examples where I have lost control. I feel myself well up as I write, surprised at how quickly I achieve this.

1. Alcohol.
2. Drugs.
3. Self-harm.
4. Suicide.
5. Lies.
6. Paranoia.
7. Agoraphobia.
8. Loss of willpower.
9. Loss of motivation.
10. Loss of self-worth.

"I am powerless, I've lost control." I read my words back to me. I then read the ten examples where I have lost control and say these out loud too. As the words leave my lips I feel a weight lift from my shoulders. The rawness and brutality strike a chord and my tears start to fall. I feel surprised at my emotion and surprised that this step strikes such a chord with me, as if this step had been written just for me. Above me are bright, beaming lights. My heartbeat quickens. I look at my shaking, scarred arms. I accept who I am and how wicked I have been to myself. I think of all the unnecessary hurt caused to myself and those around me. I feel a rush and am unable to stop the tears. A sudden sense of emotion swamps me. Feelings I haven't felt or allowed myself to feel in months come flooding back. I look at my words again and feel a release, the same release I was previously only able to find via my grisly self-harm.

September 12th – Ada

Strange dreams occupy my mind. Outside my window the low, beaming sun beats down, diminishing the heavy morning frost. The concept of time I find peculiar; some weeks fly whilst some days feel like a century, the world outside feels a million miles away.

I am surrounded by so many people yet at times am so incredibly lonely. My depression and anxiety thrive on isolation, so participation in group therapy I find important. It provides a camaraderie within our group, allowing us to identify with one another.

I have spoken on a few occasions, albeit rather briefly, but am yet to share my life story. I am working on it. I find listening to other people's stories and experiences useful. It helps with my emotional healing and makes me feel at ease that I'm not alone. I have my faults and weaknesses, just like everyone else. The more time we spend together, the stronger our bond becomes, bound together by our illnesses. As our trust grows, the more open we become as we develop a deep and sincere understanding of each other's battles and addictions.

I walk the short distance to the canteen. On my tray I place a half pint of carrot, apple and ginger juice and some scrambled egg on two slices of wholemeal toast. My appetite is dim, but I must eat. After breakfast I walk to Ellie's room and knock on her door; we hug and then go to morning group therapy together. We sit in a circle and after reading a prayer Ellie stands.

"To the outside world, my friends and family, my life was perfect, but under the surface it was crumbling. I was forever exhausted and always sad. I would sit in the bathroom as the children played and couldn't shift this dark cloud until one day, I felt compelled to self-harm.

"One morning, the children were downstairs, their screaming growing progressively louder, and I started to have these weird hallucinations and heard dim voices. I pushed my fingers in my ears, but the noises and voices were still there and then I started talking back to them. I picked up these tweezers – they weren't always in the bathroom, but that morning they were – and I pushed them into my wrist and kept on pushing until I heard a pop and I felt this overwhelming serenity and release.

"I became more and more depressed, and more and more dependent on cocaine, alcohol and self-harm to get me through each day. I would drink wine as soon as my husband left for work and the cocaine would start soon after. I would get myself in such a manic, frantic state that the only way to calm myself and feel a release was from self-harm.

"One weekend sticks out. It's early Saturday morning and we are meant to be leaving shortly for a family visit to CentreParcs. I had promised myself just one line to settle myself from the previous night, but, as we all know, that's never the case. I had been up all night from cocaine and desperate to never ever come down. It's now Saturday 7am and the children bang and thump their tiny fists on one side of the bathroom door, whilst I am slumped the other side with a bloody nose and bloody wrist.

"I hear excitement in their voices and witness the pain in their eyes as I regretfully inform them they will have to do it all without me because Mummy is not feeling very well. My husband looks at me in disgust, unsure he believes my story but too nervous to question me, deciding against another argument in front of the children as my manic mood swings and temper rises.

"Twenty minutes after they have left, he returns to our house, having left his wallet at home, to find me snorting cocaine and attacking my thighs with scissors; thankfully the kids were in the car. I love my family, I really do, but at that moment I loved cocaine and hurting myself just that little bit more. I'm worried how much damage I have done to them, to my family and to myself." Ellie sits down and we clap, we embrace, we cry.

It is early evening and I back in my room. After the day's therapy and work on Step 2, I feel more confident in my ability to confront this step. I open my book in almost excitement.

Step 2
We came to believe that a power greater
than ourselves could restore us to sanity.

I am self-destructive and dissatisfied in my own skin. My behaviour and addictions restrict me from having a wholesome and happy existence. I have no option but to seek and accept help. My life is uncomfortable. I am a coward and shy away from confrontations with my inner self and forever bury my angst under the carpet. With me everything is always tomorrow. I must act now and recover to become the person I was born to be. There is a version of me, one which I can be proud of; I just need to bring her to life and can only achieve this by editing and modifying my current being.

I acknowledge alone I am unable to change. I have tried countless times to bring change and hope; it doesn't work. I accept to progress and alter the self-annihilation patterns that have brought me nothing but pain, sorrow and sadness that I must change. Bumbling along and masking the pain with drugs, self-harm and alcohol isn't happening anymore. I'm done with it.

Being an atheist, the concept of God or any interpretation of God is hard to fathom; however, to make progress I must believe in a new perspective and greater power.

I must find a source of inspiration to help overcome my addiction. Without change comes further pain and suffering. I close my eyes. I am on a beach. I am alone. The waves are crushing against the shore and the sun shines. I observe all in front of me as the morning sun reflects the water's edge. I feast my eyes on this vastness and it strikes me. This power looms large and makes me feel insignificant. Still the waves crash back and forth against the shoreline, and I feel the power. This universe spat me out and will soak me back up.

I think of my support: Ollie, Vinnie and the people here. I am not alone. I have a higher power. My eyes remain closed; I breathe deeply. Inhale then exhale, inhale then exhale. I envisage this almighty power. I am guided and navigated to a new way of being and brought back to the person I was intended to be. I feel a sudden surge of pride, passion and new belief. There is a power much great than me; I can feel this. It brings me back to my sanity. This power will furnish me with a greater, happier existence and allow me to be reborn.

Back in my room I open the notes from my folder and, following Neville's guidelines write, "I could be happy."

I could be happy.
I could be happy.
I could be happy.
I could be happy.
I could be happy.
I could be happy.
I could be happy.
I could be happy.
I could be happy.
I could be happy.

Change is both possible and realistic. I must surrender and allow a greater power to restore, help and guide me towards becoming a better person. To change I must act, think and behave differently. I alone am not strong enough to change my existence and affect the patterns that own and destroy my life. I know this because of where I am right now. Recovery is possible and there is a solution. I believe in an alternative. I believe in a better world. I close my eyes and I sleep.

September 18th — Ada

I hear a knock at the door and a voice I recognise. Ollie stands behind the door and Kim motions for him come in. I look at him and am lost for words. He takes a chair and sits opposite me. He smiles and everything becomes a blur. My jaw falls to the floor. "I will leave you to it," says Kim as she leaves the room, giggling as I blush.

A happiness surges through me. I feel alive. We embrace, and as we hug, the tears come in waves. I cry happy tears. I feel his beating heart against mine. We hold hands and our fingers entwine. He talks, but I fail to register a word of which he speaks, as all his words mush together, melting into a beautiful melody that gives me goosebumps. His words sing to me and help ease my pain. He holds me tight and my tears don't stop. I let him in as my shame, guilt, frailty and anxiety retract. I feel overwhelmed and almost free.

We get some coffee then walk down a corridor until we reach the small wooden door which leads us into the back garden. The bright sun rises blissfully, and the air is crisp. I take his hand and lead Ollie down a small pathway until we arrive at a bench. There is no one else around. The morning air nips at the small area of visible skin from the tip of socks to the bottom of my jeans.

"You look amazing. I knew you could do this; I'm so proud of you."

I look at the floor, embarrassed by his compliment. "Thank you," I whisper softly in his ear. "Thank you, so much for everything, for not giving up on me, for helping me and bringing me here. I feel better. I feel calmer. The medication is strong, at times I'm half alive, but I've not self-harmed. I'm doing my best and following the programme. I feel like whatever is happening is working. I've missed you."

Our eyes meet. I know I am not the only one nervous. He gently touches my face, running his soft finger across my cheek, giving me a warm, fuzzy rush. He looks at me and for a split second I forget everything. He holds my waist and we hug; our tongues meet. Softly he kisses my broken lips, his kiss long and sweet. We kiss and the magic I feel is untouchable. Love sweeps though my veins and the surge of power that protrudes from each particle within me knocks me for six. He takes my hand and squeezes it tight and we kiss for what seems an eternity.

I feel giddy and stoned. For a split second I forget everything. I imagine a life without fear, a world without worry and an existence without pain. I look at him and the happiness defeats my hurt. My insides tremble. This warm feeling rushes through me and my breathing shortens. He puts his arm around me, which I choose not to resist. I feel his beating heart, which now means more to me than mine.

I look at him and I think that I can't mess this up. I can't let this pass. I simply cannot let this go and can't let him go. His pouting lips leave me in a daze. I am completely and utterly captivated; an enormous urge of well-being engulfs my whole body. Each moment we spend feels so fragile right now; each second not with him a moment lost.

Each passing thought, my worries and anxieties that rush and race around my mind, come to a stop. I choose not to think and instead choose to relax. Still we kiss and I forget the world. I feel a calmness and tranquillity take over.

Morning turns to noon and our time together has passed. Kim informs us it's time to say our goodbyes. I stare at his face, trying my best to remember it exactly as it should be, and hug him tightly, conscious not to cry. We approach the office and our hands sluggishly part like a mother letting go of her child on the first day of school.

"Don't disappear, please wait for me," I say.

Looking into my eyes, he replies, "I will wait as long as it takes, Ada, stay strong."

He places his black leather bag over his left shoulder, turns around and departs. He leaves and my breaking heart rings.

September 25th – Ada

I wake up early to the voices in my mind. They whistle and whine. I close my eyes and take deep, long breaths. The voices raise their ugly heads, they thud and thump, the drum of sorrow beats hard. I close my eyes and my breathing becomes harder and deeper. I close my eyes and take long drawn-out breaths. I am back on the beach and see the waves and the clouds and marvel at the spectacle of it all. I tingle all over in the realisation I am no longer alone; I have my higher power.

I am prepared; my opponent was not expecting this. The demons hadn't envisaged that today I would have back-up and assistance in my corner and were expecting an easy victory. Today will not be the day that a dark moment sparks a chain of events that leads me down a path of self-destruction. My exterior may look the same, but inside I am a different animal, a different machine. Today I will fight back, and you have come up against a stronger and fitter version of me. You have had your time and fun with me. I am sick of your games.

My self-destruction trigger will not be pulled, for today I am a different being. I have more self-worth and pride.

You can try again tomorrow, but trust me, I will have the support of my higher power and will not buckle, bend and fall to your demands. I am improved version of me and refuse to bow down and give in. I have found my voice. I have found an alternative to my existence and will not be defeated.

After breakfast I enter the morning therapy session, eager to start with a positive mindset. The fog of my mind levitates. Where once self-doubt and self-pity would creep in and roam amok, today I am stronger. I am no longer weak, frail and frightened. There is hope as I have admitted I cannot do this alone. I have a higher power and can connect and communicate with my feelings. I have surrendered. I have given in. Today I will be victorious.

Step 3
We made a decision to turn our will and our lives over to the care of God as we understood him.

I have adopted a new approach to life and believe if I do the right things, peace of mind, contentment and eventually recovery will be within my grasp. A power greater than myself is now with me to aid me and give me the strength I need. For too long alcohol, drugs and self-harm have been my obsession and the focus of my energy and effort.

My new focus is a spiritual path. I believe in change. I believe I will get better and will live my life in a natural state, unaltered by my addictions. By giving in to a new ideology and a higher power I understand the path I was walking was unfulfilling. Should I continue in this vein I won't get the happy ending I require.

There is a version of me, a calmer, kinder and happier version of me, and she sits within. She is underneath my current armour and biting at the chomp, eager for her release; I believe this and shall set her free. I look at instructions and pull out a piece of paper from my file; I write "I cannot do this on my own" ten times.

I cannot do this on my own.
I cannot do this on my own.
I cannot do this on my own.
I cannot do this on my own.
I cannot do this on my own.
I cannot do this on my own.
I cannot do this on my own.
I cannot do this on my own.
I cannot do this on my own.
I cannot do this on my own.

My previous existence did not work. My masterplan for living made me unhappy and anxious. I shouldn't accept and adjust to a lifetime of misery, suffering in silence. I was surviving, I wasn't living, but no longer shall that be the case.

September 30th – Ollie

My vibrating phone stirs me from my sleep. My "I am sober" app alerts me I have now been three months sober. The time is just after seven, I awake having slept well, surprised as I am each morning that my mind is no longer foggy and murky. I open my eyes; my first thought is no longer drink or drugs. I have developed a routine. I'm patient and present. I am kinder to myself. I have developed a sense of maturity and feel capable of living a life without addiction.

I don't miss the hangovers, nausea, remorse and regret. No longer do I wake humiliated and petrified, desperately trying to piece together the night before, nervous and unable to face the day ahead. I often dream of alcohol and the sensation as it takes over my defenceless, racing mind. I don't mind this, though, as no longer do I dread the morning and hours spent withering and trembling in bed, waiting for my pain and sickness to cease.

It's a fine line between being a functioning alcoholic and full-on alcoholism. I crossed it and was lying to myself. Alcohol stopped working for me. I used alcohol to escape from reality and to stop me from feeling so vulnerable. It helped blanket my pain, but I couldn't just have one or two. I wanted to drink, but drinking was making me ill. It was killing me and not working like it used to. The buzz of alcohol had diminished. There was no joy or positivity to be found at the bottom of a bottle. My life was spinning out of control. I used my alcoholism as an excuse for unacceptable behaviour.

I was terrified to live but too frightened to die. I would wake up most mornings surprised at having made it through another night. Alcohol had the better of me and was winning. I wanted to stop, but I didn't know where to turn. I was as alone and lost. My façade was cracking, and my life derailed. I was mentally drained. There came a point where I knew I couldn't continue. I was struggling and fighting an illness I would never defeat.

I was missing out on the gift of life, wallowing in my self-pity and indulging in my downward spiral. My life was at a crossroads. Moderation wasn't going to work. My mind and my body were at breaking point. I had to abstain from drinking entirely. In order to do that, I needed help. I knew there was another way to live my life; I just had to find it. It was stop drinking or stop living. Fortunately, I sought help. I turned to Julie. I needed to act, and quickly. She told me, "If you think you have a problem, you most likely have a problem."

I arrive at Highbury & Islington underground station and walk the short distance across Highbury Fields to my morning AA group. From my first session something changed, that light-bulb moment as a glimmer of hope flickered within. I walked through the door of AA that first time and the desire and need to drink was taken from me. Something clicked.

My weekly meeting became a daily meeting; I would then find two, sometimes three classes a day to attend. The fellowship gripped me. It felt good to have a fascination and addiction to something that was helping and not harming me. I became captivated and intrigued by the concept of recovery. I would listen, open-eared, in amazement at people's honesty and strength as individuals took it in turns to spill the contents of their colourful lives into our room as we fought in unison to defeat a disease that nobody ever noticed.

Every group left me feeling stronger, wiser, and my obsession began. I was told I would have to work hard for my recovery but was assured there would be help. I was given another chance and told that my life was worthwhile. I started to listen to what the people in the rooms were saying and recognised that so much of my own story was similar; their stories rang true. They had different experiences, but we shared the same feelings. I didn't feel so alone. I listened intently as they spoke of the positivity, peace and joy that sobriety has brought to their lives, now free of their addiction.

I thought no one would ever understand how I felt, but soon enough I built a bond and connection within my group. I found a safe haven, a support network and source of comfort that I could trust and lean on in times of struggle. These people took me under their wing, gave me confidence and self-belief and told me how they would help keep me sober; they helped me because someone had once guided them. The room had an aura and I felt instantly aware that listening to these people could save my life; failure to do so would result in me falling back to my old ways.

In these rooms I was able to unload the pain and hurt that had been dragging me down for too long. I would tell my story with honesty without fear or judgement and often sob and wail. I was accepted for the person I was, which allowed me to move on to a new and sober life. I asked for help, guidance and strength, and in those rooms, I found it. I learned that if those around me believed in me, then I would believe in me too. The more I put in, the more I get out, and the better I function. I have to trust a programme and process that has worked for thousands before me and in doing so believe that my life will improve.

After a few months, I was turning a corner and felt things fall into place. I examined the behaviour patterns of the whole of my life, my resentments, fears and failings.

In revealing my defects, I was able to let them go. These discoveries laid the foundation for the steps that would change me. I will take each day as it comes and tackle the problems that apply only today. Following these simple steps will result in contentment, stability and peace.

The changes to my life since finding sobriety are drastic; my world no longer revolves around drink. I wake each morning with a clear head. I work three days a week and go the gym every other day. My relationships with other people are improving. I am less selfish, putting others before me. My anxiety and depression have waned. I have more energy, focus and drive. Through sobriety I have found solace, sanity and peace.

I have rebuilt bridges, learnt to forgive myself and am doing the best I can to live as the person I was intended to be. Stopping drinking doesn't make me spectacular. I am no better, no worse than the next man I pass on the street; however, I am a better version of myself than a few months previous. I have hope, vision and can take pride in how far I have come. I've gained control of my life and can now look in the mirror without despising my reflection.

I no longer have a desire to drink alcohol and refuse to let my mind and behaviour be altered and abused by a drug that offers no benefit and am grateful to be on this journey. I have made friends from my group that I hope will always be a part of my life.

It's my group that keep me sober. I owe them my life and respect. Coming here has made me believe I am capable of being who I want to be. It has rebuilt my confidence and made the foundations of my life seem less shaky. I have the potential to be happy; I just need to believe it. I have choices and am able to dictate the story of my life. Every action and every choice has a consequence. I must remember my recovery is a process, not an event; slow and steady wins the race.

It takes strength and determination to keep going and keep coming to these classes, but I do it because I know where I will end up if I don't. I cannot allow myself to walk that journey again. Coming here and having a life without alcohol enables me to have a simple, peaceful existence. I know where one drink ends. If I pick up a drink again, I will lose everything; it's that simple. I was lucky Julie stepped in.

I enter the room and say my pleasantries. We all say a prayer. Jimmy, a tall thin man with a red nose, stands. He is wearing a tweed jacket too big for his skinny frame; he saunters around the room at a snail's pace, talking as he walks.

"Alcohol is a wicked, effective poison that will rule and control your life. It's powerful and evil. It cares not about our age, sex, religion or status. It is not discriminative. This disease will wear down the best of us and, in time, kill us; it destroys us both mentally and physically. The more we consume, the greater our dependence and the more suffering we will cause to ourselves and those around us. Alcohol will fool you and make you believe it is your friend; it is your worst enemy.

"Being an alcoholic is tedious and fearful. You are imprisoned in a hellish existence, consumed by sadness and hurt. There is no romance in waking up feeling sad and sick each morning. Alcohol does not calm us. It is a depressant. It makes us irritated, aggravated, irrational and causes our body to feel distressed. It leaves us mentally and physically broken. We are no braver when consuming alcohol. Addiction to alcohol denies us a happy, healthy existence. This self-inflicting punishment magnifies our problems and so we rely on it more.

"Ask yourself what happiness alcohol has brought you and how it enhances your existence. We don't have to be dominated and dictated to by alcohol. You need to free yourself and return to the state you entered this world, carefree, happy and relieved of stress. Don't let this disease kill you; don't let it win. Take back your future and own it.

"Don't feel shame in admitting your addiction to alcohol; be honest with yourself. We took the necessary steps to change, and set ourselves free. Today you have a choice. AA does not guarantee sobriety, but change is possible as long as you are prepared to put in the daily work. Don't be fearful of the void left by alcohol.

"Sobriety is not easy; however, habits can be broken. You just need to have the desire to break them. Approach AA with open arms and work the twelve-step programme and practise the principles of the fellowship of Alcoholics Anonymous in all your affairs, and don't take a drink of alcohol, one day at a time.

"There is hope. You can recover and rebuild your life. A different, brighter future awaits us. Allow change and enjoy recovery. Alcohol doesn't have to control you any longer. Sobriety will rejuvenate you like nothing else. Give sobriety a chance; you will discover you are a better, kinder, happier person and more at peace."

October

Ada

I wake early, get dressed and quietly stroll to the kitchen. There is no one else around. I make myself a coffee, some toast and sit alone at a table and open my book.

Step 4
We made a searching and fearless
moral inventory of ourselves.

This step scares me. I must rake up my past and bring to light what's held me back and is preventing me from living the life I should be living. It requires a personal assassination. I cannot achieve happiness and freedom until I release the past. I can only achieve inner peace by listing all my lies, secrets, wrongdoings and shame. I must face fear square in the face and fight him to allow myself to be reborn.

I refer to Neville's notes. "Your inventory is not solely focused on your fears and weaknesses but also your strengths and positive traits. To allow you to move forward to a new life, you must be aware of both your strengths and weaknesses. You don't have to complete this step in full now; just do the best you can at this moment in time. There is plenty of time to do the rest. Keep it simple; just be honest with yourself."

I have nothing better to do and time on my hands, so this morning, as painful as this might be, I shall make a start; it must be done. My first task is to write down five examples of where I am weak and where I am strong.

Weaknesses:
1. Selfish.
2. Cowardly.
3. Dishonest.
4. Insecure.
5. Chaotic.

Strengths:
1. Determination for change.
2. Respectful.
3. Generous.
4. Hopeful.
5. Forgiving.

I must then write, "The truth shall set me free." I do this ten times as instructed.

The truth shall set me free.
The truth shall set me free.

The truth shall set me free.
The truth shall set me free.
The truth shall set me free.
The truth shall set me free.
The truth shall set me free.
The truth shall set me free.
The truth shall set me free.
The truth shall set me free.

I must then list five examples of where I have felt shame and five of my fears.

Shames:
1. Failed attempt to take my own life.
2. Self-harm.
3. Failure to seek help.
4. How I spoke to Ollie.
5. How I let down Daisy.

Fears:
1. Voices in my head.
2. Social interaction.
3. What other people think of me.
4. Being alone.
5. Letting those around me down.

I am as honest as I can be, with the realisation that the more I am able to let go of who I once was, the greater chance I have of reclaiming the version of me I wish to be. I must look in the mirror and admit my failings, as dishonesty will only delay my recovery. I will let go of the underlying issues that affect my self-destructiveness and lead me down a path I don't wish to travel.

I will break down the walls and tear up the foundations. To gain control I must let go of the shackles of my past or forever they will haunt me. My past may be painful, but it will shape my future and propel me into a new life of peace. Only I hold to key to my recovery.

October 9th

A knock on the door wakes me; the time is just after 7am.

"Sorry, I know it's early – do you mind if I come in? I'd rather not be on my own right now." Ellie walks into my room. She looks sleepy and worn; her face is glum and her eyes bright red. She sits at the other end of my bed and places herself underneath my thin duvet; her cold feet touch mine, startling me.

"I don't know what's wrong with me. I feel unmotivated and aimless. I keep thinking about my babies. I dreamt about them again last night. Each morning I wake alone with the realisation that they are no longer by my side. I just want to hold them tight once more. I don't want to let them down again. I feel so hopeless and terrified. The longer I am here, the further I feel from them. They are all that's driving my recovery. I'm so scared of failure and I'm worried I will never make up for the harm I've caused.

"I worry that regardless of how hard I try that I will forever revert back to the person my family don't want me to be. I'm so scared of leaving here and being that person. I wish I could just shut my eyes and when I open them,

I'm not like this and I'm the version of me my children and husband love. I feel trapped in both body and mind; I just want to feel normal again. I don't want to feel sad or angry anymore. I feel so desperately uncomfortable in my own skin."

We walk to the kitchen. The walls are bright and punchy, and jazz music plays softly. I pour us both a strong coffee and we then go outside, where we find a seat in the courtyard. The chair is damp with dew and has flaky white paint, which sticks to my jeans. It is a beautiful morning – crisp, clear and cold enough to require a cardigan on top of my T-shirt but not a jacket.

I look up at the naked sky and hold her shaking, sweating hand, and she breaks. We sit in silence with the only sound the sobbing of a lost, broken soul. I comfort her and she rests her head on my shoulder.

"You have made such progress. Your children would be proud of you; I am proud of you. You are fortunate to be here, to have this opportunity to get better. You need to fight for yourself and for your kids. Not everyone is strong enough to realise they need help, let alone know what to do once they get it; it's not easy.

"You are capable of more than you think; just take your time and stop questioning yourself. Regardless of how noisy the voices get that tell you that you can't do this, just ignore them; you can beat this. To create anything worthwhile takes time; recovery isn't meant to be easy. Don't let the expectations of other people affect you. It's hard, but we must keep going. It's normal to think we aren't good enough or give in. It doesn't matter what has happened to you in the past. We might not get another chance like this. If you wait for the perfect moment to change you never will do. You have come too far to fail and go back to square one.

"Don't you think we all wish we could take back the pain we have caused to those we love? I do, but you can't focus on that anymore. Holding on to your past will halt your recovery. All you can focus on is today and remain positive. I'm under no illusions that I'm any better, but I'm OK with that. As long as each day we do our best, that's all we can do, right? We are in recovery; it's not meant to be a quick fix. To recover who you were, that person you want to be for your children, for yourself, is going to take time; you just need to keep doing what you are doing and stay strong."

She looks at me, reaches out and puts her heavy arm around me, bringing me closer to her; her lower lip wobbles and she breathes deeply.

"I know you're right. It's the stress and emotion of everything. I'm normally so independent; I feel so reliant on others and at times find it a little overwhelming and difficult to deal with. I know what the right path is; I'm just so scared that I'll wander off it again. This is my last chance; I'm so scared of falling backwards. I don't want to be a failure to my children; I am sober but I'm sad. Perhaps it's just this routine: breakfast, therapy, lunch, therapy, dinner, therapy."

"But that's why we are here; we all need one another. I need you just as much as you need me, so don't start getting any smart ideas of departing – you can't get out of it that easy; don't think you are going anywhere. You can't start doubting the steps or programme now. Every moment of every day I still have urges to drink, to self-harm, but I am beginning to understand the only way to give myself a chance of happiness is to follow our programme. We both know the consequences should we leave here before we are supposed to. Everyone deserves a happy life, Ellie, even you and me!"

She stops crying and laughs.

We walk the short distance to our class, where we are greeted by a new therapist. She is short, thin, and rosy-cheeked; her name is Beth. She has dark hair and teeth too large for small mouth. She informs us that this morning we shall begin with step five. She looks around the room, ensuring she has the group's attention, clears her throats and reads.

Step 5
We admitted to God, to ourselves and to another
human being the exact nature of our wrongs.

"One cannot find success in recovery if he or she continues to hide secrets, or harbours feelings of shame without the help of another. Continuing a life of secrets and hiding our past from ourselves and others prevents us from progressing. Whatever shame or embarrassment you feel, just let it all out. It is a process of you declaring your intention to change.

"Choose someone you can trust, someone willing to listen, and lift the weight of addiction and past behaviours from your shoulders. Talking to someone will help alleviate negative feelings of shame and guilt. Free the weight of your past; confession is great for the soul. Release all guilt and resentment and stop suffering in isolation.

"The purpose of this step is not to feel shame or fear but to embrace the process of deleting your past and moving on to a brighter future. Think of it as a spiritual house cleaning. It's time to unleash any dark secrets to allow us to move forward. Illuminate every dark moment; don't hold back. Be honest. Look at who you are, and who you would like to become. Accepting yourself as you are today will allow you to be free."

I unleash the skeletons of my cupboard upon Ellie. To narrate out loud to another person enhances my shame of past misdemeanours. It does, however, allow me to acknowledge, dissect and digest in detail my previous wrongdoings as my toes curl and insides turn upon reflections of reckless, regrettable incidents I would rather not revisit before Ellie shares hers with me; we cry, we laugh, we cringe.

We have no reason to feel guilt, shame or resentment. The past is the past; we can't change it. We can only shape today and our future. To hang on to the past prevents change and a positive future. By addressing of my fears, weaknesses and anxiety, and approaching these from another view, gives me a better opportunity of becoming the version of me I long to be. Left to my own devices I will self-destruct. I must stay connected to other people, to my support network.

To change I must connect with others and belong to this new community. Whilst I can work on my programme in isolation, without my network, the chances of me going back to my old ways remains high. When I am having a bad day, I can take comfort that I am not alone. I just need to remember that bad moments are a moment in time and with support I can change, I can be happy and will recover.

We take it in turns to let go of all that's been holding us back. As I listen, I feel a connection with my fellow comrades as we release our guilt and shame, allowing us the chance to become who we long to be. The more we release, the more we laugh; the more we surrender, the more we weep.

We are a tribe and come together in torment and find peace and comfort in our community. We laugh, we cry and are no longer alone. By sharing our pain, we give each other a new perspective and hope for change. We find solidarity and salvation in people who, just a few months previous, were strangers. Our demons, our skeletons and the truths that were once locked away are released, and in unleashing these upon our group we can suffer as one. We find trust and truth in one another. We are hungry and desperate for change; we become one.

October 16th

I wake early, consumed with fear. Shortly after arriving here I was told I would be asked to write my life story and tell my tale to the group. Today is the day. Whilst aware how painful this will be, I guess it's a mark of how far I have come that today I feel ready. My stomach somersaults. I put on my jeans and notice how tight they have become. I walk to the mirror. Though I have put weight on, I am able to find comfort in the context of my own skin and almost appreciate my self-worth; in the past I've been guilty of painting myself in a dim light.

I collect my notes, walk to the kitchen and find the first empty table, choosing to sit alone. I drink an orange juice, eat some scrambled egg, close my eyes and recite my notes. I walk to the meeting room, nervous in my approach. *Now or never*, I tell myself. I find a face I recognise in Ellie and sit next to her. She tells me it will be OK and holds my shaking hand. I take several deep breaths and then stand. My group, no different to me, bound together by our disease.

"Hello, I am Ada. I am an alcoholic, drug addict and self-harmer.

"Growing up my mum and dad owned various pubs in the East End of London. Alcohol felt like part of my DNA. It was always around me and part of my upbringing. My drinking began from the age of twelve, went into my teens and continued through high school and college and then into my career. Alcohol took away the shyness, my fear and made me brave. It gave me confidence and made my insides glow. It gave me strength and courage; it allowed me to dance, talk to strangers and lose all fear. I thought it helped me to be the real me. I always felt my drinking was under control; looking back, I now see it wasn't.

"My concept of an alcoholic was a grubby wino; a lost soul sat drinking from a bottle wrapped in a brown paper bag on a street corner. I was still capable of a productive day at work. Everyone I worked with drank; all my friends drank. In my eyes I didn't consider myself to be an alcoholic or even close to being one.

"On my twenty-first birthday I received a call a work: my mum and dad were involved in a car accident; my mum had died, and my dad was in hospital. A week later my father died too. They were driving back from a weekend in Devon, where they had been at a family wedding. My dad had been drinking heavily all weekend; he was over the limit and hit an oncoming lorry. It was then that my drinking accelerated. It numbed my feelings and helped me deal with the shock and aided my denial, anger, sadness and anxiety.

"Almost a year ago, I lost my best friend Daisy to cancer. My world caved in completely. Nothing made sense. The lights in my life went dim. Daisy died and drinking became my obsession and routine. I would drink to black out. My blackouts were a blessing. My whole existence became slow motion. Survival became a chore. I was forever in a haze of hurt; my insides were twisted and torn. Alcohol stopped me from thinking.

"Alcohol tore through my life, leaving a hole so large I felt it would never heal. Life became gradually harder to live. I quit my job. It became inconvenient. I spent my time drinking or hungover. Life was unmanageable and friends gave up trying to help. I feel shame and sadness for the harm I inflicted on others and the damage I caused to those relationships.

"It was around this time the cocaine abuse began. I had always socially dabbled in recreational drugs, but in a short space of time I became dependant on cocaine; it was now a necessity. It was also around this time that I discovered self-harm. I had been scattering Daisy's ashes one morning and my eyes were diverted, excited almost, by a broken bottle; in this blunt instrument I visualised release, hope and escapism. I had this overwhelming desire to hurt myself. I deserved to feel pain because I was alive and my friend wasn't; that just didn't sit right with me.

"When I was young, I had an invisible friend, shortly after Daisy died the voices returned. What would start as a dull murmur transformed into this being that would haunt me, berate me from the moment I woke to the moment I blacked out. The voices would commentate on my actions, my looks and at times tell me how worthless I was, that I'm not good enough and never will be. They would tell me it was me that deserved to die and not my friend and work me up into such a frenzy, telling me the only way I can live with myself is to hurt myself.

"I wasn't sleeping; I would go for days without shutting my eyes or eating anything. My paranoia was insane. My mood became dark. I would lose days, sometimes weeks, in my flat with the curtains closed and my only companion the ragging voices in my mind. I felt lost and alone. Fear was eating me up. I thought I was mearly weak, stupid and inferior. I was so trapped with anxiety, sadness and fear I ended up structuring my life around it.

"Self-injury became a huge part of my life. I was around this time that suicidal thoughts and urges became the norm. Every day was a battle to survive in my own mind. It became harder and harder until one day I gave in. I made a mistake of thinking I didn't want to be around anymore. My depression took over and won. I was defeated and had lost control. I decided to kill myself. I was desperate, a complete mess. My life had become unmanageable; the pain I brought on myself, looking back now, I find hard to fathom.

"I stopped worrying about dying and started to look forward to it. I didn't want to face up to life; life was scary. My mind was warped and sad. I had no fear of consequences. I just wanted an easy way out. I was so depressed and didn't care if I died. I wanted the pain to stop. The only way I thought to quieten the noises in my head, my fears, failings and guilt, was to end my life.

"One morning I decide to do it and was ready to bring down the curtains on my life. I wrote a note to my friend Ollie. The sky was bright; outside my window birds were signing, their notes high and melodic, unaware that on the other side of the wall I was about to bring my life to a sudden end in the most inhumane and ghastly manner. Looking back it all feels like a blur. It was my friend Ollie who found me; in the past he had tried to help, but I had pushed him away. I was lucky.

"I was transferred to the local psychiatric hospital, where I stayed for a few weeks. When I was discharged, I was given an aftercare pack, some numbers to call in an emergency and medication, but I needed more than that. The voices began again but this time I called for help. Fortunately, I was brought here, by my friends Ollie and Vinnie; they saved my life.

"When I arrived here my emotions were heavy and my anxiety through the roof. I feared the staff, patients and myself. I wanted to go home and deal with things myself, but my way of living wasn't working. My mind was scrambled, like a puzzle with pieces all over the place. I didn't know where to start. As each day passes, I do feel my jigsaw closer to completion.

"On my first night here, I cried. I cried again this morning, but this time it was tears of relief. I was reading through this and the progress I've made suddenly dawned on me. Being here has allowed me to face up to who I am, who I was and who I want to be. I acknowledge my previous way of living was not productive. I've told myself no longer will I allow emotions and feelings to impact me as they once did. I have learnt to let go of my past because until I let go, I will continue to hurt myself and those around me.

"I've learnt vital coping mechanisms to carry me forward and give me a sense of purpose to get up each morning, facing each day with a positive outlook. I've become more confident – only slightly, but I feel something. I don't feel quite so scared and nervous about life. Perhaps it's just my medication, but my mind feels more balanced and stable. I am not quite so jumpy and fearful of my future. I'm surviving, albeit day by day, but I am still here and determined not to revert to the person I once was. I am naturally quite an impatient person, but recovery takes time. There is no quick fix for my depression, addictions and anxiety. How I feel right now is, I will never take another sharp instrument to my skin again. I will never drink, and I will never again take drugs.

"There are many things I would like to alter in my life; so much of my past I wish I could fix, but in time I will make amends. Every day is a new awakening because I have been given another chance. I won't let my past addictions destroy my life or shape my future. I am learning to deal with things in a healthy way and I'm ready to fight for my recovery to move forward and live my life – no longer to have to suffer in silence, hurt myself or reach for the bottle. I know there is another version of me, a happier one housed inside, but only I have the tools to free her. Being here has given me a new perspective on my past; I feel more in tune with myself. Inner peace and happiness are achievable.

"I have, for the first time, thought about my future and begun to think about things I would like to achieve when I leave here. I don't feel quite so much of a burden as I once did. I realise people do care about me and maybe I'm not such a bad person after all. I don't continually need to hurt myself; no longer will I inflict wounds on myself and hurt those around me. I've decided that when I leave here, I would like to go back to college and train to be a mental health nurse. As well as wanting a better life for myself I would like to give something back and try to help others, before it's too late, as it almost was for me.

"Each morning I remind myself who I am, where I have been and where I want to go and what I'm capable of. There is a version of me who can be happy, content and who doesn't have to hate herself. I am capable of being that person and who I want to be. I am not cured. I never will be. Every day will be a challenge, but today is only one day; tomorrow can wait. There are still days when I feel down, but I remind myself that, like anything worth having in life, these things take dedication and time. I have support through the people I have met, through this programme, with help from my higher power and this community. I am slowly turning the corner. I have been given a second chance and for that I am eternally grateful." I stop talking; relief washes over me.

The group comes forward, one by one, and hug me and hold me close. My hands stop shaking, a calmness sweeps over me and tears fall. I cry for the hurt I have caused others, for the hurt I have caused myself and I cry in relief.

It's early evening and I am alone in my room. I pick up my book and rest its heavy weight against my thighs. I have reached the halfway point of the twelve steps; it has become my obsession and I find it truly fascinating. My stomach lurches and rumbles, ready for this evening's dinner, but I sit, my eyes fixated on step six of my programme.

Step 6
We were entirely ready to have God
remove all these defects of character.

To change I must find a new way of being and find happiness and joy in letting go of character defects and flaws that have been ruling my life for far too long and pushing me down a path which I have no desire to travel on. I worry about change, as change means uncharted territory; however, I'm committed to my programme and committed to change. Trusting my programme will help me find peace. I will abandon old routines and ideas that have led to ruin and despair. I write down four defects as instructed.

1. Selfishness.
2. Dishonesty.
3. Self-pity.
4. Fear.

I read my defects loudly, time after time, with an open mind intent on change, with a determination for improvement, and close my eyes. Still the defects circulate the contents of my mind but in facing these I know I can defeat them too.

Wild storms beat and lash my window. The morning sky is as black as soot. It's my birthday, but I wake with thoughts of this morning's therapy and not that today I turn twenty-nine years old. Ellie enters the room; together we walk to the meeting, where we are greeted by Beth. We spend the first few hours of the morning looking at step six. We are open and honest. There are tears, but there is hope also.

After lunch, returning to the room, Beth stands in front of the group. She opens her book and asks for silence in the room, then begins to talk.

Step 7
We humbly asked him to
remove our shortcomings.

"Humility is honesty, accepting who we are and who we could become. Without humility, there is no recovery. We must look in the mirror and recognise who we can be. In the past we have found it troublesome to see things from someone else's view. It was rare you felt responsible for any troublesome situation you might find myself in, and we would constantly look to deflect blame onto others. With a humble heart you will put others' needs before your own and in turn will find healing."

I open my notes, look at my shortcomings as recognised in step six and draw a diagonal line across each of these in a large red marker pen, then next to these I write a positive to replace the defect.

1. Selfishness – kindness.
2. Dishonesty – truth.
3. Self-pity – compassion.
4. Fear – courage.

We spend the next few hours with Beth talking openly and honestly about the changes in emotions that each of us feel and even touch on how we will cope when leaving. I look around my group and, whilst we are all in a more positive frame of mind than we were previously, a world outside these walls leaves us all feeling vulnerable and scared; I can see it in the eyes of those around me.

It's late afternoon and I am in my room. I close my eyes and drift off to sleep. The phone rings. It's Neville and he tells me he needs to see me. I worry and wonder what I have done. He opens the door and smiles; he is wearing a loud Hawaiian shirt. On the small desk in front of him sits a beautifully wrapped large package. He hands me the gift. I look at him, confused.

"So, you going to open it then? Happy birthday." He embraces me and gives me a warm hug. I tear the wrapping paper at speed to reveal a large Harrods hamper containing cheese, crackers, chocolates, duck pate and the finest tea bags from around the world. There are bags of luxurious fudge, a selection of nibbles and exquisite coffee, all housed neatly within a woven wicker box.

I walk in the dining room behind Neville. I open the door and "Happy Birthday to You" plays from a large speaker. The other patients cheer and clap upon my entrance. I feel my face turn a shade of red.

To my shock the room has been transformed into tropical beach party. I am met by an array of inflatables, palm trees, beach balls, parrots and surfboards. Some of the patients wear grass skirts. There is a DJ and every piece of furniture has been decorated in lush tropical colours.

To my left, a quartet strums ukuleles, the instruments releasing rich and resonant tones in the air as their pitch-perfect voices sing "Over the Rainbow". Behind them a big banner reads "HAPPY BIRTHDAY". To my right is a bartender in a pop-up bar serving fruity mocktails with shimmering ice, umbrellas and pineapples on sticks from tropical cups. There are pitchers of fruit punch served in coconut shells with colourful straws.

I approach Neville. "How did you afford this?"

He smiles and hands me a card.

"Ada, happy birthday, sorry I can't be there. I told you that you could do it – stay strong; you are nearly there. Enjoy your party. I miss you, Ollie XXX."

Busy staff buzz around tables and lay trays of food. There are gourmet burgers, steak and prawns, salmon skewers, and fresh salads decorated with edible flowers and a giant fruit platter. Crowds of people gather round tables, taking it turn to fill their plate with a large slathering of fine cuisine.

We apply make-up on one another, attach big silk flowers to each other's hair and spend the afternoon throwing shapes on our makeshift dance floor. Hula hoops hang from our waist and we swing our hips to happy Hawaiian beats whilst sipping on alcohol-free piña coladas.

For a split second I am lost in my surroundings. I close my eyes and Daisy is with me; my vision is blurred but I'm sure I can see her. She smiles at me with big warm lips and pulls me towards her through the mist and noise and tells me it's OK; she tells me it's all going to be OK.

November

Ollie & Ada

I awake early. The morning sky is bleak and sparse, and the air is cold. I turn up the heater in my room and pull the duvet above my head. I walk to the kitchen, fill a beige ceramic bowl with bland muesli and drown it in ice-cold milk. From the corner of my eyes I notice Ellie. She gallops towards me and wears a large smile as tears run down her beautiful, unblemished cheeks. They are happy tears. She takes the tray from me and puts it down at speed, causing my breakfast to spill, with the contents now showered across the floor.

"Thank you, Ada, thank you. John called me this morning; he said he has organised for some marriage counselling when I leave here. He said our time apart has given him time to reflect. I spoke to the children too. He told me he loves me, that he still believes in me and is proud of my progress. I couldn't have done this without you. Thank you."

We walk down the corridor and enter the morning's group. Beth stands before us; she smiles on our arrival. After a few minutes the idle chit-chat stops. The mood in the room is sombre. With eyes closed we say a prayer and hold each other's hands. We read the twelve traditions of AA then take it in turns to talk. Each share gives me goosebumps, causing the hairs on my neck to stand to attention. We break, we cry, we hug, and we clap.

"Today I would like to make a start on steps eight and nine. Please refer to the notes in your book; like all steps you will keep coming back to these and it is not expected you complete these in this room. We as individuals are works in progress; these steps are work in progress too. The purpose of this group and these therapy sessions is to bounce off one another, guide one another and help one another achieve the common goal of sobriety and change, and when we leave here, we will, of course, carry the traditions we have learnt."

Step 8
We made a list of all persons we had harmed
and became willing to make amends to them all.

Step 9
We made direct amends to such people wherever possible,
except when to do so would injure them or others.

"Making amends is good for the soul. Do not be fearful of your past. Raking up the past might be awkward but with forgiveness you can move forward. With a new perspective let go of past failings. We are capable of improving our lives. Reach deeper into yourself, be open to explore the unknown and embrace what comes along. Come clean, make amends and clear your conscience, feel better about yourself, relieve stress and let go of hostility and blame.

"Listing whom we have harmed will allow us to repair the damage we have caused and help us in creating healthy relationships moving forward. To move forward you must take ownership of your past and repair the damage done; it allows us to have a fresh start. Dealing with these situations from your past will allow you to let go of your guilt and let the healing process begin. I would like you to each choose one person and devote this session to writing a letter to them.

"Step nine gives us the chance to clean up the mess and repair the damage. For a brighter future we need to repair the past. Forgive yourself and work on restoring any broken relationships. Holding on to past concerns will play heavily on your mind and could prevent you from attaining the clarity and serenity you're working so hard to achieve. You have all made such great steps forward; remember, you are stronger than your weaknesses."

I lived my life in an irresponsible way with little regard to others. I must take responsibility for my actions and amend my behaviour patterns. I think about how Ollie must have felt when he found me. I must apologise for how my actions made him feel. With humility and calmness, I spend the session writing a letter to Ollie. I read the letter back to myself and feel a shift inside. I am changing, I know I am, and I feel a much greater connection with my feelings and am more aware of how my actions and behaviour patterns affect other people and their feelings.

Dear Ollie,

I hope you don't mind me writing. For me to move forward, I must acknowledge the hurt and pain I have caused you. I must release myself from any pain I have unconsciously been carrying. My past is my past. It is not changeable. I cannot allow it to block my future. There is no freedom without forgiveness. I cannot cling to the past. I was so hell-bent on self-destruction and self-pity that other people's feelings and emotions were ignored. I was neither kind nor considerate; instead I was mean, callous and selfish.

I'm sorry for everything I did, that you had to find me at my flat like that, how I spoke to you that time. It's not possible for my future to shine brightly unless I allow the dark from my past to be released.

For me to recover I must let go of resentment, blame and self-pity, and swallow some pride. When I arrived here, I was so angry and selfish; I had such a lack of self-care. To enable me to rebuild relationships, I need to identify the relationships that were damaged and take responsibility for my own actions. By writing these down it allows me to examine some of the same situations from another angle and perspective. I must be honest and compassionate and take accountability for my actions.

I should have been more open and honest with you. Deep down I so desperately wanted what we had to develop and go somewhere. You made everything

OK, but I worried, and my anxiety and wicked thoughts kicked in. I knew for sure that in time I would let you down. I can be so selfish and thought being on my own meant I was unable hurt anyone else. Being on my own allows me to do as I please, when I please and be answerable to no one. It was difficult to reach out to you because I had been so spiteful and you were going through enough; I'm sorry.

My chaotic brain, intent on causing maximum carnage, would not allow me to believe I could be happy and that someone might like me. I was fearful of rejection and I felt this burden and empowering guilt about Grace too. I was just stuck forever underneath a black roaring sky. I buckled underneath my woes. Every minute I ached as my troubles hung heavy, gnawing at my mind.

I lost all faith in everything and was no longer living; I was simply surviving. When you're vulnerable and raw for so long, it gets daunting. I was sinking and stuck in the middle of the sea with no saviour. My grief would sting, all day every day. We are told that following loss, it makes us realise how precious life is and to make every second count; when Daisy passed, I felt the opposite. My lows were so low, I found it difficult to fathom or digest how other people are able to live with their grief. Everything we strive for, happiness, joy and contentment, I questioned if they would ever come again and quickly came to the conclusion they would not. I lost all strength and could weather the storm no more.

I was so bloody-minded. I couldn't see the wood through the trees. I didn't think about other people's feelings or emotions; it was all me, myself and I. I chased and romanticised things that made me feel content, using drugs and drink and self-harm to please me, unaware of the destruction and horror it caused for those around me. Naively I thought my behaviour was acceptable; I understand now this wasn't the case.

Having had time to reflect I will no longer push my anxiety under the carpet and try to paint a pretty picture of a painful situation. I must face my addictions each day; failure to do this will cause me to fail. I know what I am, who I am and I know I will get found out unless I follow my programme. But I am no longer alone; reaching out to my support network will help. I am lucky: I have found the root of my problems, what caused me to be unhappy as I know what it brings me.

I hope you can forgive me. I'm not sure I can ever repay you but will try my best to do so; that's all I can do.

Ada XXX

November 12th – Ollie

I read her letter. I read the letter again, this time at a slower pace, digesting every word. It brings a tear to my eye. I'm excited but nervous about what happens next. Cycles are hard to break. Whilst our bodies are now both clean, our addiction remains. I'm fearful of jumping into something too soon and worry I could increase the pressure on her and the weight on her shoulders. For one person to engage in a relationship after recovery is hard; for two it's problematic. I'm scared of her relapse, of my relapse and either one of us losing control. I worry past behaviour patterns could infiltrate our relationship.

We are both damaged and both require healing. Ada's rock bottom might have been more severe than mine, in her attempt to take her own life and rehabilitation, but we are on the same page; being aware of each other's past should make the struggle easier. We must stay realistic, inspire one another, embrace each other's faults and work together to look forward, not backwards.

I'm neither naive nor oblivious to understand that the odds of future bliss with Ada aren't stacked in our favour but hope we can use the pain and hurt from our past to propel us to a brighter future. We must forget the past and focus on today, think differently and commit to a new way of being, one of sobriety and peace. We must repair the damage we have suffered and create a bond based on respect and trust. In times of trouble we must confide and communicate in one another to give us a fighting chance for change.

I'm unable to change mine or Ada's past; however, I can affect today and can change tomorrow. Our relationship can take a backseat; it's our recovery that must take precedent. For too long we have put up with the horrors; it's time to experience life's highs. I'm hopeful the skills Ada has learnt from her time away will ensure she stays free of addiction and free of pain. We are not alone; ensuring we follow our programmes, we can grow. We must be honest, patient, let our past go, become open and work on being a better version of ourselves, and in times of pain, frustration and rage must protect one another and get through the situation safely. I want to help Ada reintegrate into society and believe that together we can create a brighter future for us both.

November 21st – Ada

Lucid, twisted nightmares wake me, leaving me feeling off-balance, alone and overwhelmed. I ponder my return home and picture in my mind my scarce, naked flat. A wave of anxiety surges through me as unwelcome thoughts return to cloud my panic-stricken mind. I feel trepidation and tense at the prospect of leaving here, lost, and worry whether I possess the psychological strength to get through the initial months of sobriety. I dream of self-harm. I dream of drinking. I dream of drugs.

I fear how I will deal with the transformation back into community living and society. I haven't conquered my addiction and my recovery doesn't end when I leave here; life after leaving is when my real recovery begins. My time here has revealed things I was previously unaware of. I need to remove the blinkers to see life for what it is and take responsibility for my actions.

I'm impatient and find it difficult to consider my future when I'm so frequently informed to take each day at a time. When I leave here, I will have to start again, do it all from scratch. I have a fresh start and blank page to work from but am aware that dreams are often not all they cracked up to be. I don't want to relapse and fear the humiliation and shame of a setback. I can't go back to square one and for all this hard work to amount to nothing.

My time here has been based on a schedule; I've enjoyed the routine of always having somewhere to be at a certain time. Having too much spare time on my hands is dangerous with my mind. I'm going to miss the routine of rehab, the friends I have made and the support I have received, the stark contrast to my life before I came here. I will miss the protection, and the safety net I have here; by going home I give up that protection.

There is always somebody to talk to here; there won't be at home. I'm scared where to start, having been down this road before only to let myself down. Returning to the real world will expose me to temptations and cravings. I'm returning to the same environment that drove me here and must face my addictions on a daily basis. I'm worried what a sober life means and how I will cope with the boredom. The process of recovery is lifelong. I found solace in my substance abuse; without a replacement I wonder what will happen? I guess I'm cynical about the chances of success when I think about previous wrongdoings. It's frightens me to face a new way of coping when I have been so used to using my past addictions to mask any pain or worries, aware how quickly I could sabotage the efforts of my previous hard work.

It's late afternoon and I walk to another group, based around triggers. A lady called Kathy introduces herself.

"Life after rehab can be difficult, as you are leaving your support system behind and we must understand the challenges that lie in wait. Transitioning after rehab and the entire recovery journey can be complex. It's important to be able to recognise the signs of relapse. No matter how strong you feel, we're only human and are susceptible to giving in to temptation or past behaviours. We need to develop an understanding of how relapse occurs, and by developing an understanding of the process this will allow us to administer the right action to prevent relapse triggers and show us what behaviours to look out for.

"Leaving rehab is an exciting time, but it also means facing a number of challenges. Being here is a start and your recovery does not end when you leave here. The real challenge is being back home and exposing yourself to the real world. Rehab is the first step in a long journey. Today I want to focus on how best to prepare for when we leave and move back home. If we are not ready, the transition can be a perilous one; preparation is the key to your success.

"I have an exit plan for you and have put together a collection of books I feel will be of benefit to help educate yourselves about your addiction and how best to prepare you for the outside world. Educating ourselves will help recognise potential triggers and allow us to understand what we are feeling and what to expect, helping to guard yourself against the coming difficulties in the weeks and months that lie ahead."

We are each handed our exit plan and a variety of books with colourful covers.

"Do not be fooled into thinking you are cured, leaving here under the illusion that you are now permanently fixed; this complacency will lead to relapse. Full recovery does not happen overnight. Your recovery is a work in progress. Don't try to take on too much at once. This is still a fragile time, and the slightest thought of failure or not living up to expectations can trigger disappointment and a potential relapse. Take time and be patient; keep in mind the bigger picture and keep your head focused on one day at a time in your recovery.

"The most critical aspect of a successful long-term recovery is developing a new mindset. Stay busy to keep your mind focused on productive activities and away from negative feelings. Become more self-aware to be able to recognise these signs of relapse; plan a daily and weekly schedule. Keep the momentum going from being here but remain realistic and set realistic expectations to keep focused on the path of recovery."

We work in groups and spend the next few hours identifying and writing down our triggers, deciding what to do in these situations as each trigger comes up, helping and protecting ourselves, and working with Kathy to identify what strategies or techniques we can use so we are better equipped to overcome them.

Step 10
We continued to take personal inventory and
when we were wrong promptly admitted it.

"You must surrender to the sanctuary of your programme, observe your learnings and ensure your past is put to good use. This step is about growth and laying the foundation for your future. Identifying dangerous emotions will allow you to conquer your shortcomings. Think of step ten as being handed instructions for life, a continuation of everything you have learnt thus far, a troubleshooting guide to keep you at peace."

The group spend hours digesting the information, working on our worries and shortcomings, and confiding in one another. We talk of strength, determination, hope and of change.

In turn we stand, reminding ourselves of our faults and failings, but strengths too. We work on our self-awareness so when conflict and crisis cloud our minds we are better equipped to stay on course with our recovery.

Returning to my room I re-read the triggers from my earlier class. I re-read the two steps previous and, deep in thought, digest the information to hand. I'm cautious but confident that this self-assessment will allow me to see any mistakes prior to making them and allow me to focus on how to improve my life and the lives of those around me.

December

Ollie & Ada

Roaring thunder wakes me as forks of lightning brighten the dull morning sky. I walk to the kitchen, passing lost souls staring motionless at the large TV in front of them as they flick from channel to channel, looking for something to focus their attention on. I pour a large coffee and grasp the mug tightly to warm my cold hands. I put on my jacket, pull my hood above my head and walk to the pond. I walk and breathe deeply as the morning air rushes and fills my nostrils and lungs, waking my senses as a howling wind hits my cold, pale face. The morning fog is thick and hazy, and the dark, ominous clouds hang heavy above.

Clumps of mud stick to the base of my high-top canvas boots as my feet squelch in loose earth. I push past wild twigs and broken branches until eventually I find my bench. I sit and I stare as driving rain beats on the water's edge. I take a sip of my coffee; I look at my wrists and notice the difference from when I arrived. The scars I wear remain but are fading. The rain has stopped, and the water is now silent, the only noise the morning birds. Their song is sombre. I enjoy coming here, being alone, with time, when I can think. I close my eyes.

I think about the past, the future, about being a functioning member of society once more, and I worry about my lack of defence mechanisms. I'm fearful of leaving here, having my independence handed back to me and letting myself down, aware of the pain I'm capable of causing myself. I fear living a conventional life and worry as I am unpractised in living in the real world. I worry about the everyday tasks.

Ollie consumes my thoughts, making it difficult to think about anything or anyone else. He is in my heart and in my head. I'm scared of opening myself up for failure, of loving him and him leaving me, so frightened of what could go wrong. I'm apprehensive and worry that being here has created even more distance, and I'm conscious how painful it can be to fall in love with somebody who doesn't love you back.

My emotions change daily and today love frightens me. The thought of love and relationships confuses me; I find it taxing and difficult to understand. What if two human beings trying their best isn't enough and Ollie and I end up worse than before? I want to grow individually, and with him also but worry he might not be up for the ride? What if I'm too much? I fear he might just be in love with the idea of being in love.

In order to love another, I must first learn to love myself, but I am progressing with this. I need to be cautious and protect myself and not act on an impulse. I guess I'm nervous a relationship could derail my progress; I worry I will become attached and that the thought of him leaving will destroy me and could trigger a relapse. I don't want to be selfish and need to give myself and Ollie a chance. I need to treat this as a new relationship, with the respect it deserves, but approach it with caution and delicacy.

I'd spent so much time alone prior to meeting Ollie, unaware of how intense it was to be in a relationship. It scares me to feel like this about someone. To lower and loosen my self-defence mechanisms scares me. I want him to realise I was worth the wait, and share my bright outlook. I must forget my weakness, my complexity, my faults, that I am unhealed, needy and unattractive, and instead focus on my strengths.

I will be noble, brave and hopeful. I will let him in, allowing each other to build ourselves once more. I won't give in or allow defeatist thoughts to overcome the joy and contentment that I know awaits me. I am committed to creating a brighter future. I am worthy of happiness. Nothing good comes easy. I will remain positive and remember there is much to gain. I want Ollie to be an important part of my life but cannot become emotionally dependent on him; there must be a balance.

To allow our relationship to become a priority and lose focus of my life is dangerous. I was told to protect myself, not get into a relationship for at least a year after leaving here and to look after number one, but that's easier said than done. I am not naïve and am aware of my fragility, but with Ollie I feel calm. For every story of heartbreak there is one of happiness. I have made mistakes in my past, but this doesn't feel like one of them. I need to trust him, trust myself and roll the dice.

The shining light emerges from drifting, dark, heavy clouds as the morning begins to show itself. The sun shines through the bushes as bright, beaming light warms me. I look at the water's edge and capture the splendour and the magic of it and the nature that circulates all around me, and I feel a glow. The darkness fades away and illuminates everything as beaming colour fills me with joy and jubilation as my worries and woes that once silenced and stopped me in my tracks are washed aside. I look up at the sky and I feel light and positivity, and I know that the future I crave is there, but it will not just be handed to me. I must fight for it. I know I can do this. I will beat this; I have come this far and am a capable person able to achieve a life of worth, a happy existence, but it comes down to me. I must have faith and the belief that good times are waiting and the hurt that I have encountered and the road that I have travelled has to amount to something. I stand; still the sun beams, I feel myself pulled further from the darkness as my mind transfixes on a brighter outcome.

I walk back to the unit for my morning therapy; I take in my surroundings and observe all life before me. The place is alive as catering staff buzz around, feeding hungry mouths, and caffeine-desperate souls pour strong coffee with heavy hands, seeking their first hit of the day. I look at the new faces; they look back, nervous, frightened, consumed with sorrow. Still I stare and am instantly transported back to my arrival and remember how I felt when I arrived here. I give them an encouraging smile, hopeful that they will last as long as I have been able to.

Beth welcomes us into the warm room, where we sit tightly in a semicircle as she clears her throat then softly speaks.

Step 11

We sought through prayer and meditation
to improve our conscious contact with God as
we understood him, praying only for knowledge
of his will for us and the power to carry that out.

"We must put my faith in our higher power, our support network and our programme. Staying connected to a new perspective will allow us to move forward. We will use our strengths to overcome our struggles. Surrendering ourselves will lead to satisfaction and success, freedom and relief. Honesty with our higher being will allow us to breathe and progress and offer us as individuals the happiness and contentment we deserve. Connection to our higher power on a daily basis will help us grow spiritually. Let prayer and meditation calm us and reduce the fears that threaten our recovery. No longer are we alone. Continued reliance on a higher power and programme lays the groundwork for our recovery, for without it we will be lost."

The habit of prayer must become a way of life, and in moments of chaos and confusion I will ask for guidance. With a support network I can consult others when I'm not able to do this alone; I must remember I am not alone anymore. If some days I'm missing the courage, humility, gratitude and courage I need for my programme to work, I can use my higher power and those around me to aid me. I will not be afraid in asking for help from something beyond ourselves, to ensure I have the right answers to get me through the day.

I close my eyes and I breathe. I feel calm and take deep breaths as my mind gently wanders to a calmer environment. I remove myself from the outside world. I close my eyes and think about how fortunate I am to still be here, to be given a second chance; I will ensure I now help those around me, those still suffering from this disease. I remind myself how much time I have spent in this programme and what I have accomplished thus far. I have reprogrammed and refocused my mind and I will use my positive energy to help those around me still suffering. I ask for help from my higher power to heal. I ask that I am blessed with honesty.

December 12th – Ada

My heart beats fast; the thumps and thuds become relentless. My hands are cold, and my damp forehead sweats profusely as my stomach somersaults. I am nervous, anxious and feel like I could chuck my guts up at any moment. The day has arrived. Today I will be leaving. I have mixed emotions. It is the day I have been waiting for but fearful of also.

I feel an overwhelming sense of pride and joy at what I have achieved but am nervous of the world that waits outside my window and leaving the safety of my surroundings, for I have forgotten how to be free.

The time is just before noon and Kim gently knocks on the door. "Time's up, honey."

My hands clam up. I feel my legs shake and take a final look around my room. It looks bigger, warmer and more inviting than when I arrived. I walk to bathroom. I open the cupboard above the sink, ensuring I have everything, then take a final glance at my home and look in the mirror. I tell myself I can do this. I have come too far to fail. I will not break. I will stay positive and walk out with my head high, proud of my achievement and how far I have come.

I collect my bags and carry them to the front of Neville's office. I knock on his door; he welcomes me in. His smiles at me and out of nowhere tears fall from my eyes. "Sorry, I'm sorry," I say. He wipes my tears, and we hug; we hug for what seems an eternity.

He takes a deep breath and looks at me.

"It's hard for me to articulate just how proud I am of you, Ada. You have been through so much but are still here. I can tell by the look on your face how nervous you are, but please trust me, it will be ok. Recovery is a long process – don't rush; change takes time. Don't expect to leave here with every problem solved; recovery is a day-by-day process.

"It will take time to get back to the life you had before your addiction, but you aren't alone. There is help, encouragement and support all around you. Stay focused on staying clean. Be patient and calm. Devote everything to rebuilding yourself; there is nothing as important as you. I know what you can achieve and what you are capable of. Recognise how brave you are. I look at the person I see before me today and think back to the shell of a person that sat before me four months ago, that frightened, nervy, anxious girl with the weight of the world on her shoulders, too heavy for her nimble frame. You looked like you would buckle at any minute.

Believe in yourself, Ada. Follow the steps. Forget the past and keep moving forward to a brighter future. Breaking addiction is a challenge and fear is natural, but you can do this. I have high hopes for you. Just take things easy and work honestly with your programme. Be kind to yourself and understand change takes time. You don't have to be afraid anymore. There is a whole world outside of here that is waiting for you. You have proved what you can do. Follow this programme and you have nothing to fear.

"Within this folder are all your notes and contact numbers; you have my personal number too. As I said on your first day here, my door is always open. You can achieve anything you set your mind to. Recovery is not for those who need it but for those who want it." He stands up and hugs me goodbye as tears fill my eyes.

We embrace and my tears dampen the shoulder of his linen cream shirt. I thank him for everything and take the short walk to my final therapy. As I enter, Ellie and the rest of the girl's clap. We say a prayer and read the twelve steps, the twelve traditions, and I look around the room and stand for my final chair.

"As you know, today is my final day. Whilst I am excited to share my new ideas and attitude that I have learnt here, I am nervous. I am nervous and scared of relapse; I am nervous of breathing the outside air. I am nervous of being alone and am nervous of becoming the version of me who came here. When I arrived here four months ago, I was lost and imprisoned in my own mind. Whilst I have made progress, I know I am only one bad decision from a return to the person that arrived here and always will be.

"Letting go of all my hurt means I can look at myself

in the mirror and not want to scratch my own eyes out. I feel less anxious and even a little more mature. I now understand that things don't have to be the way we don't want them to be. I won't let the bad days drags me down, as I am in charge, I am in control and more in tune with my emotions to make any situation better.

"Whilst nervous to leave, I do feel I will be stronger and like I have more in the tank so I can fight back when chaos reigns and self-pity tries to sabotage me. I feel like my life is more manageable. I have a new perspective to help when problematic patterns and triggers arise. Being here reminds me I am not alone. I feel I have a better understanding of what treatment and recovery means and would like to take the knowledge and understanding I've gained to help and motivate others.

"I just wanted to say thank you to all of you for putting up with me, for listening to me and helping me. I feel truly blessed to have met you all and I hope we can stay in touch on the other side."

As I sit down my bottom lip shakes and the group form a circle around me; we embrace and in unison we cry. It all comes out, the hurt, the pain, the relief, the fear, the pride, the hope and sadness, the pain in letting go and leaving this group and the journey which we have walked together.

We compose ourselves, form a circle and sit with books open, digesting and working on step twelve, the final step.

Step 12

Having had a spiritual awakening as a result
of these steps, we tried to carry this message to addicts
and to praise these principles in all our affairs.

The world in which I exist does not revolve around me. I was so caught up in my own life the thought of thinking about others seldom crossed my mind. Going forward I will be less self-centred and help others and will commit to a different way of living.

I can't be humble and honest and free of my past failings if I am shallow and selfish.

I will carry the message of recovery, help others who are still suffering and work with others who are still struggling. Being of service reminds me of where I once was and where I no longer wish to be.

I would like to help and inspire others, offering them the same kindness I received, and then encourage them to pass on what I've learned. In time I would like to be a sponsor and share my experience and hope. No one understands the programme and journey to recovery as well as someone who has been through it, loathed it and loved it. I would like to pass on the principles of my programme, to carry the message of recovery to other people. Giving service to others would give my life a new purpose and meaning and help safeguard my recovery.

Ellie gets take a blue biro pen and writes down her phone number. She looks at me with bloodshot eyes. "Thank you, thank you for everything. Your friendship, hope, words and wisdom. I owe you more than you will ever know. You supported me and were my shoulder to cry on. You listened and believed in me when it felt like one else would. You made me feel like it was OK to be me. I will miss you. You have gone above and beyond. I will miss our morning cups of coffee. It's an honour to have met you and to be able to call you a friend. I hope everything works out for you with Ollie, and you get the life you deserve. We hug and she kisses me on the cheek. We both cry; our tears collide.

I sit and wait impatiently; after several minutes a taxi pulls up and Ollie gets out of the vehicle. He smiles and waves at me. I run towards him and bury myself in his arms. My insides dance and I realise how happy I am to see him. He holds me, I feel elation and my anxieties decrease. My face flushes and heart thumps. I feel the adrenaline pump inside me. He holds me and a wave of warmth rushes over me as we are reunited.

He puts my bags in the boot and we are now sat side by side. He takes my hand and as he holds me, every ounce of sadness that once resided in and burnt the bottom of my belly is swept away, replaced with a warm rush of love and lust. All the hurt, anger and pain that suffocated, swamped, and smothered me is released as wave after wave of indescribable, glorious, hope, energy and joy circulates through me. I take a deep breath. I turn and look at the building for a final time, my sanctuary and dependency, and wave furiously at my newfound friends as the misfits huddle on the step and scream and shout and wave and jump in my direction while we move further along the gravel driveway until they disappear from my view completely.

He looks at me, and he does it in a way that makes me feel wanted and worthy; his kind, caring eyes look right through me, and my flaws and failings are overlooked. I hold his hands and I feel an energy pass between us; everything becomes slow motion, my heart is at bursting point, and I am consumed with love and desire. I am transfixed to a state of trance. He looks at me with his open, dilated eyes that well up as he talks. "I'm so proud of you." I feel unique, special and on a high only discovered previously from my past addictions, but this high is natural and pure and it levitates me, and I feel myself grin. He keeps on staring and as he does, I feel belief, trust and hope. He talks but I fail to focus on the words as my mind focuses instead on his blissful tones as his voice becomes softer, more tender, and I feel a growing sense of contentment. Still he holds my hand. I close my eyes and dream of our tomorrow.

December 15th – Ollie

Droplets of rain patter on the glass, making it difficult to see the world outside my bedroom window. I spend the early morning tossing and turning, unable to sleep, impatient to see her. I wait until 8am, then walk into the front room and see her tiny frame snuggled on my sofa's edge. "Ada? Ada? Are you awake?"

"I am now," she says quietly as she slowly wakes.

She turns to face me. There is a colour in her cheeks. Her lips look more voluptuous and her teeth straighter than I recall. She stands up, pulls me towards her and buries her face deep into my chest. The tips of her fingers delicately caress mine as our hands meet and I feel her warmth, her touch I find exhilarating. As I hold her skinny frame my frantic mind calms, my stomach somersaults and I feel giddy inside.

We gaze at each other and are lost in this moment of sheer bliss. Our lips meet, noses collide and warm tongues touch. We kiss and I feel the spark between us as we hold each other still. I feel a surge rise through me of ecstasy, contentment and an overwhelming sense of joy. I feel her racing heartbeat through her thin T-shirt, beating in sync with mine.

"I promise I won't ever hurt you again. I'm so sorry I almost let what we had slide away. Being away has given me perspective. I don't know what this is, but I like it and I want more of it. I want it to grow. I don't want we have to fizzle and fail. Before meeting you, I was worried how to act, for fear of being judged or ridiculed. I feel different now. I'm not so sure I could have allowed myself to get close to someone who hadn't been through what we have been through. You've witnessed me at my worst; I'm sorry."

Ada then looks at the looks down at the floor, slightly embarrassed by her words. I look at her and I know she means exactly what she says. I trust her. My heartbeat speeds up, my palms sweat, and I feel gratitude that she is beside me. I speak gently to her.

"After leaving you at rehab, I remember sobbing in the back of the taxi, pleading with Vinnie to go back. I thought I alone could mend you. I guess I just wanted you back. I knew I couldn't, and I had to leave you. I'm sorry I left you. There's nothing more painful than seeing someone you care for hurt themselves. The pain and sadness I felt watching as you deteriorated broke me. I'm so happy you are here. That you are back. That you are getting better. I understand I can't be your focus right now, that you need to focus on you first, but I just want you to know I'm here when you need me, when you are ready. I care for you, I really do. I have your back."

Looking up at me she replies, "That's so sweet of you.

I care for you too, more than I think you know. I feel like I am getting better. Thank you for being there for me. It makes me feel safe. I'm just wary. I'm so scared of my past addictions threatening us and threatening you. I don't want to hold you back or halt your happiness, or my demons to deteriorate your dreams. I'm sorry for everything I did and put you through and what you had to witness.

"I previously housed so much hurt and pain. But I feel for the first time in a long time that I am OK with being me and I'm comfortable in my own skin. I don't want to press the self-destruct button anymore. I no longer want to be scared. When I first met you, I wasn't ready to think about anyone or anything else. I thought if I gave you my heart and you broke it then what would happen next? What if once the novelty of me, of us, wore off and my flaws flared up, these butterflies died? If I were to open up and give you my everything, let go of my soul, convinced I was falling with the right person and we stumbled and broke and fell, then where would that have left me? I was just frightened and fragile. Scared of rejection, loneliness and you discovering the real me. Scared as I knew the excitement and anticipation would no doubt in time turn to anger, resentment and hurt.

"I feel different, though, now, and the time away and help I received is what I needed. I feel like that headspace has helped. I want to be fun, spontaneous and to open myself up. I trust you, but more importantly I finally trust myself. For the first time since losing Daisy I feel ready to share myself and my time. I'm ready for sacrifice. The thought of making someone else happy, makes me happy. I don't feel quite so selfish. When I'm with you everything makes sense and I feel a purpose. Realising that I can be happy and realising everything is possible is a wonderful thing.

"I feel like this journey I have been on, the hurt, desperation and pain, had to lead me somewhere. I know I have work to do, to be a better person; I guess we both need to grow, but I want to grow with you. I feel energised and content. Sitting here with you, my heart has rarely beat so fast. I'm just excited; you make me feel excited. I get it. It's not going to be easy. There are no guarantees. But don't you think we deserve some happiness? We have endured enough pain and hurt. I don't know what will happen or what our future is going to look like, but I just want to be here, with you, for you to hold me and for us to enjoy whatever this is, enjoy today and forget about the past or what awaits us around the corner. I can't promise much, but I promise I will give it my all. I just hope that that is enough. I hope that I am enough."

Her soul is on the line. She is raw and exposed; she is honest and open. I look at her; she is still broken, but she will be OK – we will be OK. I feel passion and desire tinged with obsession and a highly charged state of consciousness. I hold her, and this feeling tickles me all over, a highly charged sensation. It just feels right and familiar. I would sacrifice everything for her, and I believe the feeling is mutual.

December 21st – Ada

Boozed-up brides-to-be scream and shout from our carriage, high on life and champagne, ready for their big night out as our train pulls into Brighton train station.

Ollie looks at me with his warm, sparkly eyes as butterflies rush through my body. He is wearing a double-breasted navy overcoat and black, pointed brogues. I look at him and feel pride that he is by my side. He holds me and makes me feel content. We get off the train, weaving through crowded flea markets, and walk carefree down cobbled streets, passing sweeping rows of grand Regency terraces and smart grass lawns before we arrive at the pier. Momentarily we stop to watch a Punch and Judy show before spending the next few hours on fairground rides. We play penny slot machines, eating sugary candyfloss, and share a carousel.

It's early evening and we pass a busy bar tucked away on a side street off the seafront. It has whitewashed walls, a thick carpet and famous retro record album sleeves housed within thick bronze frames on smokey red walls.

"Ollie, can you wait here? I need the bathroom."

I lie. I have an ulterior motive for coming here, but I need to do it. It's simply something I must do. I walk into the bar and take a deep breath, nervous in my approach as Saturday evening crowds barge and bruise against me. My palms sweat. The barman is handsome; he flutters his eyes at me as he shakes his cocktail mixer vigorously in my direction. I ignore his piercing stare, taking greater interest in the vast array of gin, vodka, rum and whisky which sit neatly housed on the glass shelves behind him. I look at the gin and imagine it swimming its way past bulbous ice cubes and pushing past a fresh slice of citrusy lemon before the rush of it hitting my waiting, pouted lips.

I feel giddy and excited at the anticipation of the blackout that awaits me. Still I stare at the bottle. I feel myself shake and perspire. All background noise fades, and the room becomes slow motion as my troubled mind is transfixed and whisked away in a state of trance. The crowds of people and bar staff all blur into one and become ghosts. It is just me and the poison. I turn around and Ollie is outside, playing with his phone, unaware of my battle that lurks within.

"Gin, please, large." My words leave my lips before my mind is able to decide.

The barman informs me, "Coming right up."

I focus on the empty glass and feel my insides throb as I hear the glug of the clear, expensive bottle hit the empty glass soon to be mine. Still his eyes stick to me working their way quickly from my eyes to my chest as he slowly pours, releasing the contents of the glorious bottle and filling my glass. I watch in fascination as every drop hits my goblet.

"I haven't seen you here before. What's your name?"

I ignore him, smiling nervously as my mind concentrates on the beautiful sight that beholds me. He slides the glass to my direction, turns, then walks away. I now have both hands tightly clamped around the glass. I hold it and it feels like a long-lost friend. It warms me. I play with and caress the now-smaller ice cubes and stare at the glass.

I take a deep breath then pull my glass closer to my lips. I put my nose on the edge and can now smell the potent fumes and strength of the liquid in my possession. The mixture has not masked the gin; still the smell lurks, ready for my consumption. The petrol-like fumes send a shiver down my spine. From nowhere unwelcome voices haunt me once more.

"You want this, Ada. You deserve this. You didn't think I was leaving you for good, did you? Just have this one; it won't harm you. I know you want me; have some fucking balls, woman, and take me, take me whole, take all of me, let me take you to that place you long to be, to oblivion, to blackout – that's what you want. It's waiting for you; your happy place is here. Take me down in one and let me set you free.

"Let me taunt and tame you once more; let me take control. I know who you are; I know your dirty secrets. This is who you really are and all you will ever be. You are weak, insignificant, for it is I who is in control. Give me that control, Ada, give me that power. I own you, Ada, and always will."

Clutching the glass with a shaking hand I bring it closer still. The rim of the glass thuds against my teeth so the liquid now wets my dry lips. I shudder and shake; I feel goosebumps all over and inside I scream, I shriek, but the words don't come out. The bar is packed, but I am alone. Still I hold the glass; I run my tongue around its lip. I am lost in the noise. Still I breathe deep. The voices get louder and are now screaming and shrieking. They become so loud I cannot mask them anymore.

I need to quieten them, so I push my head back and I pour the glass with shaking hands; my mouth is now full and the strong poison startles and stings my cheek and the roof of my mouth. The alcohol burns my throat and the insides of my cheeks and I can now feel people looking at me and they are laughing, and I am drenched in darkness and I am transported to the guilt, the pain, my comfort, and I am back here.

I run to the toilet and I spit the contents of my mouth out, and I realise in this moment this is not who I am anymore, this is not who I will ever be. I am free, and I laugh and spit again, and I push my fingers down my throat. I gag and I fill my mouth with cold, clean water. I look in the mirror, wipe my watering eyes and look back at who I am, who I have become, and I think of Daisy and Ollie, and most importantly I think of me: I am stronger, fitter, happier, healthier. I own me. I am in control and am now comfortable looking at my own reflection. I run out of the pub into Ollie's open arms and hold him tight.

"Are you OK?"

I look at him; he touches me, and I feel my heart ignite and hammer as my insides are soaked in euphoria. "I am now, thank you."

We lock hands and walk on the pebbled beach towards the sea. With every step the pebbles crunch and shift beneath our feet. Hungry seagulls swarm above, beating their wings, hopeful of snatching day-trippers' scraps from open fish and chip boxes. The stormy sea is empty but for a few brave paddleboarders wincing as they navigate their way around breaking, roaring waves. We sit still and soak it all in, watching in awe as the cold, stormy sea fizzes and bubbles. I breathe in and taste the salty ocean air, feeling it travelling up my nostrils. My teeth chatter as the angry sea crashes onto the shore. Beside me Ollie looks enthralled, with eyes widened. We huddle against one another; he shelters me from the storm with his thick coat as we watch the waves gurgle and collide. He puts one arm around me in hope of warming me. I speak.

"If someone had told me a few months ago we would

be here now, in this moment, clean, happy, hopeful and excited, I would have laughed at them. I love being back in the real world and being here with you. I love getting to know you again. It feels different this time. I will cherish this moment. I wish we could stay like this forever."

He looks at me, nervous. He goes to speak then stutters before finally his words come out.

"Ada, I'm falling for you. I want to help you succeed; I want to help you to stay happy. I just want to be with you. I've had this infatuation with you from that first moment you answered the door at Julie's. I just want you to know you are my favourite person. We have things to work on; life isn't meant to be easy, but we can get there."

I see in his expression the admiration and desire he seems to have for me. I look into his eyes and feel a transformation taking place inside me. I feel a state of bliss, exhilaration and calmness. My insides glow and I feel an instant warmth within, a sense that maybe things could work out and that perhaps life is slowly falling into place.

We sat transfixed, watching the sky as night draws in and the waves continue to crash into one another, tasting the breeze blowing from the tide. I cling tightly to Ollie. The cold breeze stings my eyes, causing me to squint, so I close them and rest my head on his shoulder, feeling my heartbeat accelerate.

I look out far into the sea and in doing so feel the pain of my past leave me. I breathe deeply, listening to the percussion of the waves. Still we cling to one another, content and calm with nothing to fear. The waves roll in, vicious and fearsome, the only noise that of flocks of starlings congregating on the old pier. I gaze out to the water's edge with someone I am beginning to love, and I know it's going to be OK. My heart tightens. I hold him tighter still, Ollie, my shining light when sadness soars.